ENGINEERS SERIES WAGON FLEET

DB970000 – DB

(Second Edi

compiled
John Dickenson
and
Peter Ifold

Published by:-
South Coast Transport Publishing
Hampshire, England

Printed by Itchen Printers Ltd.
Southampton. Tel: (0703) 227161

ISBN 1 872768 12 1

Since this photograph was taken "Tope", ZCV, DB970403, a 22T Ballast Hopper Wagon, has been withdrawn. It is seen in happier circumstances at Perth on 1st August 1989. Paul W. Bartlett

"Rudd", ZBV, DB972000, a 21T Ballast Sleeper Wagon, is pictured at Hitchin on 5th May 1990. Paul W. Bartlett

Engineers Series Wagon Fleet (DB970000 - DB999900)

Introduction

This publication covers the Engineers Fleet No's DB970000 - DB999900 and is the second edition. It records all wagons in the number series remaining in service on British Rail at the end of February 1994 together with wagons withdrawn since June 1993. In accordance with standard practice withdrawn vehicles are indicated by (W). Since the last edition was published in November 1989 there have been considerable changes on BR with further changes to come with government plans for the complete privatisation of Britain's railways. Whilst this publication in no way reflects the future plans it was felt appropriate to change the title.

Wagons operated by the Engineering Sections of BR have prefix letters applied to identify the "owning" section. All engineering service stock carry a D prefix in addition to a "regional" letter which identifies for whom the stock was built e.g. DB = BR-built stock. A third letter is added at the front of the prefix to identify the "owning" section. The "owning" prefixes appropriate to this publication are as follows:-

A = Director of Mechanical & Electrical Engineering
L = Director of Mechanical & Electrical Engineering
(BRB HQ Electrification Projects)
R = Director of Research
The addition of no third prefix letter = Director of Civil Engineering

TOPS (Total Operating Processing System) was introduced by BR in 1972 and each vehicle was allocated a three letter TOPS code. In respect of codes allocated to stock included in this publication the following letters apply:-

1. First letter = main type group
   Y Service, bogie freight
   Z Service, 2-axle freight

2. Second letter = Sub-division of main type

3. Third letter = Brake type
   A Air Brake
   B Air Brake, through vacuum pipe
   H Dual AFI and Air Brakes
   O No Brake (Hand Only), unfitted
   P No Brake (Hand Only), vacuum pipe only
   Q No Brake (Hand Only), air pipe only
   R No Brake (Hand Only), dual air and vacuum pipe
   V Vacuum Brake
   W Vacuum Brake, through air pipe
   X Dual Brake (air and vacuum)

Throughout this publication the TOPS and Design Codes for each number series together with the Tare Weight and Gross Laden Weight (G.L.W.) are applicable to all wagons within that series unless indicated otherwise. Readers should note the weights expressed in the description are imperial tons though the tare and gross laden weights reflect metric tonnes.

Although TOPS Codes have been applied generally to all wagons since 1972, the Engineering Departments have continued to use "Marine" codenames. Where appropriate these codenames are shown in the descriptions to the appropriate number series.

During the 1980s BR commenced a build programme involving the construction of a large number of "Turbot", "Tope", "Rudd" and "Clam" wagons. These were conversions from surplus "B" - Prefixed vacuum braked stock. Wherever possible we have included for these types the numbers of the wagons on which these conversions were undertaken and these are shown to the right of the current number in brackets. Unfortunately in a few instances the former number was not available. We have also included the former number of tank wagons where this was available.

The "Manta" (DB975500-7) and "Marlin" (DB975508-33) Long Welded Rail Carriers which were rebuilt in 1970 from SR EMU underframes have been excluded from this publication. Details can be found in "Departmental Coaching Stock" also published by S.C.T. Publishing.

The compilers wish to acknowledge the photographic contributions made by Paul Bartlett.

John Dickenson
Peter Ifold

April 1994

Number Series: DB970000 - DB970059

Description: 22T Ballast Hopper Wagon
Builder: RFS Doncaster
Tare Weight: 8.5t 8.9t !%
Design Code: ZC003A ZC003B # ZC004A =
ZC005A * ZC005B - ZC005C %
ZD151A +

Converted: 1987-88
G.L.W.: 30.0t 30.5t -
Tops Code: ZCV ZDV +
Fishkind: "TOPE"

DB970000	(DB426213)	DB970020	(B426380)	DB970040+	(DB430806)
DB970001	(B433409)	DB970021	(B433738)	DB970041	(DB432972)
DB970002+	(B426031)	DB970022	(B426840)	DB970042=	(DB430799)
DB970003	(B428116)	DB970023	(B433300)	DB970043	(DB425152)
DB970004	(B430890)	DB970024	(DB427443)	DB970044	(DB427410)
DB970005	(B414019)	DB970025	(DB428263)	DB970045	(DB427729)
DB970006 W	(B427963)	DB970026	(DB425714)	DB970046	(DB433380)
DB970007+	(B430896)	DB970027	(DB426391)	DB970047+	(B430980)
DB970008+	(B423177)	DB970028	(DB424862)	DB970048	(DB421705)
DB970009+	(B420023)	DB970029	(DB426038)	DB970049	(DB426942)
DB970010	(B428288)	DB970030	(DB420304)	DB970050	(DB431912)
DB970011	(B428642)	DB970031	(DB431337)	DB970051	(DB432502)
DB970012	(B415956)	DB970032	(DB429450)	DB970052	(DB426449)
DB970013	(B431783)	DB970033	(DB419990)	DB970053	(DB427195)
DB970014	(B425828)	DB970034#	(DB430562)	DB970054	(DB432748)
DB970015	(B420543)	DB970035	(DB431600)	DB970055	(DB422630)
DB970016	(B433244)	DB970036	(DB432406)	DB970056	(B423629)
DB970017*	(B340231)	DB970037	(DB428053)	DB970057-	( )
DB970018	(DB432211)	DB970038#	(DB430303)	DB970058-	( )
DB970019	(DB418052)	DB970039	(DB426395)	DB970059-	( )

Number Series: DB970100 - DB970855

Description: 22T Ballast Hopper Wagon
Builder: RFS Doncaster
Powell Duffryn
Tare Weight: 8.5t 8.9t !%
Design Code: ZC003A ZC003B # ZC004A =
ZC004B ! ZC004C ^ ZC004D :
ZC005A * ZC005B - ZC005C %

Converted: 1989-91
G.L.W.: 30.0t 30.5t -
Tops Code: ZCV
Fishkind: "TOPE"

DB970100	(DB433010)	DB970118*	(DB340707)	DB970136	(DB433188)
DB970101	(DB422748)	DB970119*	(DB340856)	DB970137-	(DB340763)
DB970102	(DB431042)	DB970120=	(DB340902)	DB970138*	(DB340014)
DB970103#	(DB430228)	DB970121*	(DB340618)	DB970139	(DB433451)
DB970104	(DB426376)	DB970122*	(DB340351)	DB970140%	(DB340124)
DB970105	(DB432727)	DB970123*	(DB340116)	DB970141:	(DB340517)
DB970106#	(DB430651)	DB970124*	(DB340339)	DB970142*	(DB340591)
DB970107	( )	DB970125*	(DB340271)	DB970143	(DB432862)
DB970108	(DB421123)	DB970126%	(DB340095)	DB970144*	(DB340274)
DB970109	(DB422570)	DB970127*	(DB340409)	DB970145*	(DB340588)
DB970110	(DB431034)	DB970128*	(DB340020)	DB970146	(DB429503)
DB970111-	(DB340129)	DB970129	(DB432422)	DB970147	(DB415766)
DB970112%	(DB340130)	DB970130*	(DB340006)	DB970148-	(DB340224)
DB970113%	(DB340144)	DB970131*	(DB340855)	DB970149-	(DB340196)
DB970114*	(DB340300)	DB970132!	(DB340749)	DB970150	(DB433542)
DB970115%	(DB340356)	DB970133	(DB432810)	DB970151	(DB429043)
DB970116-	(DB340519)	DB970134*	(DB340821)	DB970152*	(DB340056)
DB970117*	(DB340631)	DB970135*	(DB340872)	DB970153*	(DB340479)

DB970154* (DB340047)
DB970155 (DB432828)
DB970156 (DB432226)
DB970157* (DB340404)
DB970158% (DB340199)
DB970159* (DB340038)
DB970160! (DB340405)
DB970161 (DB431550)
DB970162* (DB340584)
DB970163 (DB427303)
DB970164* (DB340060)
DB970165* (DB340401)
DB970166 (DB432070)
DB970167* (DB340713)
DB970168 (DB432656)
DB970169- (DB340729)
DB970170* (DB340012)
DB970171* (DB340822)
DB970172 (DB431457)
DB970173* (DB340007)
DB970174* (DB340158)
DB970175! (DB340636)
DB970176 (DB422478)
DB970177* (DB340354)
DB970178- (DB340132)
DB970179* (DB340123)
DB970180* (DB340104)
DB970181* (DB340176)
DB970182 (DB432855)
DB970183 (DB431167)
DB970184 (DB427001)
DB970185 (DB432489)
DB970186# (DB430655)
DB970187# (DB430406)
DB970188* (DB340011)
DB970189* (DB340074)
DB970190 (DB433512)
DB970191 (DB432184)
DB970192 (DB425380)
DB970193= (DB430531)
DB970194 (DB426329)
DB970195 (DB433621)
DB970196 (DB422020)
DB970197 (DB428028)
DB970198 (DB427002)
DB970199 (DB433085)
DB970200- (DB340229)
DB970201 (DB423207)
DB970202 (DB425784)
DB970203 (DB428674)
DB970204 (DB418058)
DB970205 (DB432417)
DB970206 (DB432589)
DB970207* (DB340010)
DB970208 (DB431507)
DB970209 (DB422579)
DB970210! (DB340703)
DB970211 (DB425554)
DB970212 (DB432673)
DB970213 (DB432892)
DB970214= (DB430665)
DB970215* (DB340448)
DB970216= (DB430596)
DB970217 (DB426657)
DB970218 (DB423545)
DB970219 (DB433534)
DB970220 (DB429553)
DB970221 (DB419132)
DB970222% (DB340694)
DB970223 (DB432203)
DB970224 (DB429490)
DB970225* (DB340839)
DB970226! (DB340731)
DB970227* (DB340285)
DB970228* (DB340096)
DB970229 (DB428414)
DB970230 (DB427280)
DB970231* (DB340025)
DB970232 (DB432617)
DB970233 (DB432601)
DB970234# (DB430614)
DB970235 (DB423492)
DB970236 (DB429013)
DB970237* (DB340832)
DB970238* (DB340883)
DB970239* (DB340260)
DB970240 (DB432758)
DB970241- (DB340345)
DB970242- (DB340446)
DB970243- (DB340539)
DB970244- (DB340594)
DB970245 (DB432622)
DB970246- (DB340638)
DB970247- (DB340369)
DB970248-W(DB340363)
DB970249* (DB340206)
DB970250: (DB340798)
DB970251- (DB340350)
DB970252- (DB340277)
DB970253- (DB340186)
DB970254- (DB340195)
DB970255- (DB340308)
DB970256- (DB340502)
DB970257- (DB340734)
DB970258- (DB340254)
DB970259- (DB340771)
DB970260- (DB340864)
DB970261- (DB340257)
DB970262- (DB340217)
DB970263* (DB340783)
DB970264- (DB340681)
DB970265- (DB340138)
DB970266- (DB340601)
DB970267! (DB340040)
DB970268- (DB340428)
DB970269* (DB340031)
DB970270- (DB340299)
DB970271* (DB340906)
DB970272! (DB340834)
DB970273 (DB413959)
DB970274- (DB340440)
DB970275= (DB340500)
DB970276- (DB340160)
DB970277- (DB340214)
DB970278# (DB340381)
DB970279- (DB340533)
DB970280- (DB340510)
DB970281- (DB340162)
DB970282 (DB432185)
DB970283! (DB340843)
DB970284* (DB340909)
DB970285- (DB340543)
DB970286- (DB340399)
DB970287- (DB340513)
DB970288: (DB340518)
DB970289- (DB340365)
DB970290- (DB340524)
DB970291 (DB431820)
DB970292- (DB340627)
DB970293- (DB340246)
DB970294- (DB340511)
DB970295 (DB431068)
DB970296* (DB340596)
DB970297 (DB426992)
DB970298- (DB340505)
DB970299 (DB340389)
DB970300 (DB432331)
DB970301- (DB340207)
DB970302 (DB429644)
DB970303= (DB430785)
DB970304- (DB340661)
DB970305# (DB430537)
DB970306- (DB340344)
DB970307- (DB340058)
DB970308- (DB340282)
DB970309- (DB340531)
DB970310- (DB340544)
DB970311- (DB340168)
DB970312- (DB340329)
DB970313- (DB340322)
DB970314- (DB340552)
DB970315* (DB340077)
DB970316- (DB340298)
DB970317- (DB340334)
DB970318- (DB340443)
DB970319= (DB000000)
DB970320- (DB340135)
DB970321 (DB432063)
DB970322# (DB430660)
DB970323 (DB428069)
DB970324# (DB430424)
DB970325 (DB425768)
DB970326* (DB340327)
DB970327* (DB340026)
DB970328 (DB433423)
DB970329* (DB340173)
DB970330 (DB432379)
DB970331 (DB433450)
DB979332* (DB340296)
DB970333* (DB340178)

DB970334 (DB432178)
DB970335 (DB427120)
DB970336* (DB340289)
DB970337% (DB340504)
DB970338 (DB429692)
DB970339 (DB433603)
DB970340% (DB340494)
DB970341 (DB427735)
DB970342 (DB426209)
DB970343 (DB433176)
DB970344 (DB427482)
DB970345 (DB426497)
DB970346 (DB428993)
DB970347 (DB426453)
DB970348 (DB420240)
DB970349 (DB426473)
DB970350- (DB430607)
DB970351 (DB429995)
DB970352 (DB427034)
DB970353 (DB423897)
DB970354 (DB426685)
DB970355 (DB432872)
DB970356 (DB432724)
DB970357 (DB426288)
DB970358 (DB428154)
DB970359 (DB431968)
DB970360 (DB433381)
DB970361 (DB427944)
DB970362 (DB432910)
DB970363* (DB340796)
DB970364- (DB340455)
DB970365: (DB340397)
DB970366* (DB340032)
DB970367* (DB340773)
DB970368* (DB340317)
DB970369* (DB340059)
DB970370*W(DB340019)
DB970371 (DB431854)
DB970372- (DB340092)
DB970373 (DB426503)
DB970374= (DB430792)
DB970375 (DB422486)
DB970376 (DB416311)
DB970377 (DB428449)
DB970378 (DB418013)
DB970379 (DB432446)
DB970380 (DB427422)
DB970381 (DB424219)
DB970382 (DB432209)
DB970383 (DB431429)
DB970384* (DB340607)
DB970385# (DB430109)
DB970386 (DB429474)
DB970387 (DB427365)
DB970388 (DB430340)
DB970389 (DB432091)
DB970390 (DB426208)
DB970391 (DB426901)
DB970392 (DB432744)
DB970393 (DB423595)

DB970394 (DB426536)
DB970395 (DB423117)
DB970396 (DB426728)
DB970397 (DB424952)
DB970398 (DB424857)
DB970399 (DB425240)
DB970400 W(DB432193)
DB970401* (DB429912)
DB970402 W(DB431375)
DB970403*W(DB430267)
DB970404 (DB432325)
DB970405 (DB426315)
DB970406 (DB432320)
DB970407 (DB420303)
DB970408 (DB426066)
DB970409 (DB428126)
DB970410 (DB420587)
DB970411 (DB427860)
DB970412 (DB427279)
DB970413 (DB428089)
DB970414 (DB419183)
DB970415 (DB426534)
DB970416 (DB425221)
DB970417 (DB423709)
DB970418 (DB423217)
DB970419 (DB427492)
DB970420 (DB427028)
DB970421 (DB424879)
DB970422 (DB428159)
DB970423- (DB340269)
DB970424% (DB340430)
DB970425% (DB340654)
DB970426% (DB340134)
DB970427% (DB340483)
DB970428% (DB340613)
DB970429% (DB340316)
DB970430% (DB340197)
DB970431% (DB340159)
DB970432% (DB340573)
DB970433% (DB340755)
DB970434% (DB340292)
DB970435% (DB340265)
DB970436% (DB340484)
DB970437% (DB340717)
DB970438% (DB340089)
DB970439% (DB340161)
DB970440% (DB340148)
DB970441% (DB340145)
DB970442% (DB340478)
DB970443% (DB340457)
DB970444% (DB340143)
DB970445% (DB340492)
DB970446% (DB340799)
DB970447% (DB340675)
DB970448* (DB340087)
DB970449% (DB340677)
DB970450% (DB340325)
DB970451- (DB340318)
DB970452% (DB340420)
DB970453% (DB340315)

DB970454% (DB340391)
DB970455- (DB340541)
DB970456% (DB340250)
DB970457% (DB340630)
DB970458% (DB430598)
DB970459-W(DB340656)
DB970460% (DB340695)
DB970461% (DB340603)
DB970462% (DB340582)
DB970463%W(DB340736)
DB970464* (DB340064)
DB970465 (DB431816)
DB970466 (DB432585)
DB970467 (DB432100)
DB970468! (DB340042)
DB970469* (DB340166)
DB970470^ (DB428998)
DB970471 (DB432947)
DB970472- (DB340745)
DB970473 (DB433142)
DB970474 (DB431667)
DB970475 (DB433744)
DB970476 (DB433274)
DB970477 (DB433261)
DB970478- (DB340249)
DB970479: (DB340542)
DB970480 (DB424305)
DB970481 (DB433036)
DB970482 (DB422688)
DB970483 (DB431462)
DB970484 (DB426672)
DB970485 (DB433108)
DB970486 (DB432554)
DB970487 (DB462769)
DB970488 (DB422723)
DB970489 (DB433262)
DB970490 (DB429004)
DB970491 (DB423579)
DB970492 (DB432305)
DB970493 (DB423175)
DB970494 (DB422552)
DB970495 (DB427271)
DB970496 (DB429404)
DB970497# (DB430074)
DB970498* (DB340722)
DB970499: (DB340556)
DB970500 (DB420883)
DB970501 (DB423241)
DB970502 (DB424302)
DB970503! (DB340181)
DB970504 (DB426065)
DB970505 (DB425570)
DB970506 (DB429620)
DB970507* (DB340735)
DB970508 (DB432757)
DB970509 (DB424649)
DB970510: (DB340486)
DB970511 (DB431585)
DB970512= (DB430779)
DB970513 (DB433421)

DB970514* (DB340251)
DB970515*W(DB340481)
DB970516 (DB428963)
DB970517= (DB430740)
DB970518 (DB427079)
DB970519 (DB426269)
DB970520 (DB340027)
DB970521* (DB340829)
DB970522- (DB340191)
DB970523 W(DB433159)
DB970524* (DB340667)
DB970525 W(DB432619)
DB970526* (DB340099)
DB970527* (DB340876)
DB970528* (DB340063)
DB970529 (DB433206)
DB970530* (DB340386)
DB970531 (DB425148)
DB970532 (DB430963)
DB970533- (DB340213)
DB970534 (DB433157)
DB970535 (DB428078)
DB970536 (DB432916)
DB970537 W(DB426903)
DB970538 (DB422558)
DB970539 (DB431755)
DB970540- (DB340494)
DB970541 (DB430814)
DB970542* (DB340302)
DB970543- (DB340461)
DB970544 (DB427311)
DB970545* (DB340853)
DB970546=W(DB430195)
DB970547 (DB433115)
DB970548=W(DB430670)
DB970549* (DB340777)
DB970550-W(DB340208)
DB970551- (DB340774)
DB970552 W(DB432322)
DB970553* (DB340243)
DB970554*W(DB340730)
DB970555 W(DB425797)
DB970556 (DB426390)
DB970557 (DB431681)
DB970558 (DB433415)
DB970559 (DB425765)
DB970560-W(DB340394)
DB970561 (DB426423)
DB970562 (DB431860)
DB970563 (DB427371)
DB970564 (DB431372)
DB970565 (DB425892)
DB970566 (DB429573)
DB970567 (DB433351)
DB970568 (DB431829)
DB970569 (DB427669)
DB970570 (DB424225)
DB970571* (DB340885)
DB970572 W(DB423634)
DB970573= (DB430684)
DB970574 W(DB428106)
DB970575 W(DB427676)
DB970576* (DB340827)
DB970577*W(DB340808)
DB970578* (DB340358)
DB970579* (DB340599)
DB970580 W(DB433094)
DB970581 W(DB431757)
DB970582 (DB426040)
DB970583 (DB423469)
DB970584 (DB426360)
DB970585 (DB421733)
DB970586=W(DB430344)
DB970587 (DB426295)
DB970588*W(DB340801)
DB970589 (DB426522)
DB970590% (DB427305)
DB970591 (DB422504)
DB970592 W(DB433739)
DB970593 (DB428346)
DB970594 W(DB426987)
DB970595 W(DB431556)
DB970596 (DB428206)
DB970597 (DB426143)
DB970598 (DB425639)
DB970599 (DB425324)
DB970600 (DB424698)
DB970601 (DB426171)
DB970602 (DB423959)
DB970603 (DB433364)
DB970604=W(DB430781)
DB970605 (DB425147)
DB970606 W(DB427928)
DB970607-W(DB340142)
DB970608 W(DB433406)
DB970609! (DB340816)
DB970610-W(DB340572)
DB970611: (DB340724)
DB970612 W(DB422563)
DB970613 W(DB433548)
DB970614#W(DB430422)
DB970615* (DB340723)
DB970616 (DB432026)
DB970617! (DB340800)
DB970618 (DB432437)
DB970619 W(DB422622)
DB970620 (DB421647)
DB970621 (DB429733)
DB970622 (DB432013)
DB970623 W(DB422721)
DB970624# (DB430163)
DB970625 (DB421595)
DB970626 W(DB433616)
DB970627* (DB340076)
DB970628 (DB423684)
DB970629 (DB424861)
DB970630 (DB428637)
DB970631 (DB426887)
DB970632 (DB426549)
DB970633 W(DB428468)
DB970634 (DB424535)
DB970635 (DB423735)
DB970636 (DB433393)
DB970637 (DB426316)
DB970638 (DB424498)
DB970639 (DB428162)
DB970640 (DB426739)
DB970641 (DB429583)
DB970642 (DB425770)
DB970643- (DB340705)
DB970644:W(DB340121)
DB970645- (DB340155)
DB970646- (DB340456)
DB970647!W(DB340910)
DB970648-W(DB340429)
DB970649 (DB433549)
DB970650-W(DB340665)
DB970651=W(DB430604)
DB970652 W(DB422740)
DB970653 W(DB432327)
DB970654 (DB429508)
DB970655-W(DB340462)
DB970656=W(DB430122)
DB970657- (DB340545)
DB970658- (DB340670)
DB970659# (DB431019)
DB970660 W(DB433288)
DB970661 W(DB433175)
DB970662=W(DB429867)
DB970663 W(DB432196)
DB970664 (DB431777)
DB970665* (DB340590)
DB970666- (DB340131)
DB970667- (DB340687)
DB970668- (DB340454)
DB970669* (DB340471)
DB970670- (DB340435)
DB970671- (DB340424)
DB970672: (DB340608)
DB970673 (DB433454)
DB970674* (DB340765)
DB970675 (DB426042)
DB970676 (DB428052)
DB970677- (DB340154)
DB970678: (DB340779)
DB970679* (DB340653)
DB970680! (DB340379)
DB970681 (DB428512)
DB970682 (DB424706)
DB970683 (DB427763)
DB970684 (DB416133)
DB970685- (DB340357)
DB970686- (DB340589)
DB970687- (DB340117)
DB970688: (DB340818)
DB970689# (DB430298)
DB970690 (DB431616)
DB970691 (DB423971)
DB970692 (DB430831)
DB970693 (DB423714)

DB970694= (DB430463)
DB970695* (DB340635)
DB970696 (DB425576)
DB970697 (DB425133)
DB970698 (DB422715)
DB970699 (DB427742)
DB970700 (DB433228)
DB970701 (DB425786)
DB970702= (DB430532)
DB970703- (DB340320)
DB970704= (DB340416)
DB970705 (DB340340)
DB970706 (DB423375)
DB970707 (DB430803)
DB970708# (DB430427)
DB970709 (DB432761)
DB970710 (DB427348)
DB970711 (DB427618)
DB970712 (DB427367)
DB970713 (DB433647)
DB970714 (DB425446)
DB970715 (DB421566)
DB970716 ( )
DB970717* (DB340678)
DB970718 (DB429764)
DB970719 (DB433143)
DB970720 ( )
DB970721 (DB433607)
DB970722 (DB433255)
DB970723 (DB430836)
DB970724 (DB433124)
DB970725 (DB425444)
DB970726- (DB340480)
DB970727- (DB340247)
DB970728- (DB340275)
DB970729 (DB426991)
DB970730 (DB432637)
DB970731 (DB433384)
DB970732* (DB340760)
DB970733- (DB340676)
DB970734! (DB340651)
DB970735* (DB340175)
DB970736* (DB340343)
DB970737^ (DB340361)
DB970738* (DB340045)
DB970739 (DB432161)
DB970740 W(DB433448)
DB970741- (DB340114)
DB970742* (DB340617)
DB970743- (DB340402)
DB970744 (DB431505)
DB970745- (DB340419)
DB970746 (DB427625)
DB970747 (DB427993)
DB970748* (DB340290)
DB970749* (DB340611)
DB970750 (DB432940)
DB970751 (DB431989)
DB970752 (DB432370)
DB970753! (DB340005)
DB970754! (DB340690)
DB970755# (DB430330)
DB970756 (DB431512)
DB970757 (DB432090)
DB970758 (DB423737)
DB970759 (DB426132)
DB970760 (DB432764)
DB970761 (DB422510)
DB970762# (DB430445)
DB970763 (DB416054)
DB970764 (DB428409)
DB970765# (DB430283)
DB970766= (DB429921)
DB970767* (DB340004)
DB970768 (DB427800)
DB970769 (DB431222)
DB970770 (DB426973)
DB970771 (DB431804)
DB970772 (DB424252)
DB970773 (DB426356)
DB970774 (DB433612)
DB970775* (DB340487)
DB970776 (DB423297)
DB970777 (DB433073)
DB970778 (DB426674)
DB970779 (DB427665)
DB970780 (DB428474)
DB970781 (DB428522)
DB970782 (DB423232)
DB970783 (DB432361)
DB970784 (DB432864)
DB970785 (DB431996)
DB970786 (DB425238)
DB970787 (DB427306)
DB970788 (DB426794)
DB970789 (DB432514)
DB970790 (DB422581)
DB970791 (DB429416)
DB970792* (DB340200)
DB970793 (DB431905)
DB970794 (DB431880)
DB970795 (DB433385)
DB970796 W(DB421946)
DB970797 (DB422671)
DB970798 (DB425741)
DB970799 (DB433605)
DB970800 (DB423505)
DB970801 (DB433259)
DB970802 W(DB420747)
DB970803 (DB421935)
DB970804: (DB340794)
DB970805 (DB429395)
DB970806 (DB433050)
DB970807 (DB433521)
DB970808 (DB426183)
DB970809 (DB427978)
DB970810 (DB433465)
DB970811# (DB430315)
DB970812 (DB421593)
DB970813 (DB425754)
DB970814 (DB432206)
DB970815 (DB428341)
DB970816 (DB425393)
DB970817 (DB431463)
DB970818# (DB430638)
DB970819 (DB423894)
DB970820 (DB432588)
DB970821 (DB419688)
DB970822 (DB423655)
DB970823 (DB426776)
DB970824 (DB423662)
DB970825* (DB340555)
DB970826 (DB431995)
DB970827 (DB428888)
DB970828 (DB428336)
DB970829 (DB431975)
DB970830- (DB340468)
DB970831 (DB426419)
DB970832 (DB432885)
DB970833 (DB426856)
DB970834 (DB427619)
DB970835 (DB429028)
DB970836 (DB430755)
DB970837* (DB340770)
DB970838 (DB417798)
DB970839 (DB420847)
DB970840 (DB429018)
DB970841 (DB421922)
DB970842 (DB432811)
DB970843 (DB426309)
DB970844 (DB425859)
DB970845 (DB422410)
DB970846 (DB432314)
DB970847 (DB426839)
DB970848 (DB426656)
DB970849 (DB421981)
LDB970850 (DB422550)
LDB970851= (DB430224)
LDB970852 (DB426754)
LDB970853 (DB426278)
LDB970854 (DB425900)
LDB970855 (DB425260)

Number Series: DB972000 - DB972799

Description: 21T Ballast Sleeper Wagon
Builder: Marcroft Engineering
C C Crump Ltd
Converted: 1989-91
Tare Weight: 10.0t
G.L.W.: 31.0t
Design Code: ZB001A ZB001B = ZB002A + ZB003A # ZB003B *
Tops Code: ZBV
Fishkind: "RUDD"

DB972000+ (DB433555)
DB972001 (DB419902)
DB972002 (DB427385)
DB972003 (DB422533)
DB972004 (DB429611)
DB972005 (DB431309)
DB972006 (DB431868)
DB972007 (DB432376)
DB972008 (DB432391)
DB972009 (DB433123)
DB972010+ (DB433163)
DB972011 (DB432687)
DB972012+ (DB432418)
DB972013 (DB432638)
DB972014 (DB431906)
DB972015 (DB433485)
DB972016 (DB431214)
DB972017 (DB433676)
DB972018 (DB429632)
DB972019 (DB423087)
DB972020+ (DB431149)
DB972021 (DB427228)
DB972022 (DB418056)
DB972023 (DB424752)
DB972024 (DB430244)
DB972025 (DB431182)
DB972026+ (DB431886)
DB972027 (DB432035)
DB972028 (DB431515)
DB972029 (DB423796)
DB972030 (DB423793)
DB972031 (DB424438)
DB972032 (DB427048)
DB972033 (DB427397)
DB972034 (DB430050)
DB972035* (DB430184)
DB972036 (DB429688)
DB972037 (DB425217)
DB972038 (DB431247)
DB972039 (DB427092)
DB972040 (DB432571)
DB972041 (DB433338)
DB972042 (DB428509)
DB972043 (DB426050)
DB972044 (DB423393)
DB972045 (DB423694)
DB972046 (DB426138)
DB972047 (DB423306)
DB972048 (DB428332)
DB972049 (DB423900)
DB972050 (DB432495)
DB972051 (DB429613)
DB972052+ (DB432330)
DB972053 (DB426993)
DB972054 (DB418188)
DB972055 (DB424516)
DB972056 (DB430523)
DB972057 (DB424990)
DB972058+ (DB427289)
DB972059+ (DB428403)
DB972060 (DB427551)
DB972061+ (DB431858)
DB972062 (DB422199)
DB972063 (DB423120)
DB972064 (DB425490)
DB972065 (DB424215)
DB972066# (DB429819)
DB972067 (DB424735)
DB972068 (DB427912)
DB972069 (DB428001)
DB972070 (DB423676)
DB972071 (DB427440)
DB972072 (DB423191)
DB972073 (DB428446)
DB972074 (DB425711)
DB972075= (DB429920)
DB972076= (DB430479)
DB972077 (DB422063)
DB972078 (DB422516)
DB972079+ (DB431592)
DB972080 (DB428902)
DB972081# (DB430238)
DB972082 (DB424377)
DB972083 (DB427242)
DB972084 (DB428021)
DB972085 (DB428932)
DB972086# (DB430770)
DB972087+ (DB432434)
DB972088 (DB428211)
DB972089+ (DB433411)
DB972090+ (DB431062)
DB972091 (DB425614)
DB972092 (DB425258)
DB972093 (DB424655)
DB972094# (DB429814)
DB972095 (DB428219)
DB972096 (DB427812)
DB972097 (DB424327)
DB972098 (DB427957)
DB972099 (DB425989)
DB972100+ (DB427810)
DB972101+ (DB431282)
DB972102 (DB432505)
DB972103 (DB432897)
DB972104 (DB425717)
DB972105 (DB425838)
DB972106 (DB430177)
DB972107 (DB427355)
DB972108 (DB427081)
DB972109 (DB426619)
DB972110 (DB426034)
DB972111 (DB423538)
DB972112 (DB426807)
DB972113 (DB428407)
DB972114 (DB425086)
DB972115 (DB426223)
DB972116 (DB433671)
DB972117 (DB423947)
DB972118 (DB432876)
DB972119 (DB425015)
DB972120 (DB427094)
DB972121 (DB429410)
DB972122 (DB423923)
DB972123 (DB416446)
DB972124 (DB424355)
DB972125 (DB424703)
DB972126+ (DB433371)
DB972127# (DB430118)
DB972128 (DB428176)
DB972129 (DB426328)
DB972130 (DB433055)
DB972131 (DB427277)
DB972132 (DB424306)
DB972133 (DB425604)
DB972134 (DB423391)
DB972135 (DB426974)
DB972136+ (DB433080)
DB972137 (DB423833)
DB972138+ (DB431921)
DB972139 (DB424827)
DB972140+ (DB427285)
DB972141 (DB425438)
DB972142 (DB427750)
DB972143 (DB419950)
DB972144 (DB426294)
DB972145 (DB427861)
DB972146 (DB433463)
DB972147 (DB428243)
DB972148 (DB423115)
DB972149 (DB423405)
DB972150 (DB432183)
DB972151 (DB432067)
DB972152 (DB420281)

DB972153 (DB431341)
DB972154 (DB432537)
DB972155 (DB425656)
DB972156 (DB431859)
DB972157 (DB429569)
DB972158 (DB424637)
DB972159 (DB425962)
DB972160 (DB432104)
DB972161 (DB427035)
DB972162 (DB431189)
DB972163 (DB426145)
DB972164 (DB427458)
DB972165 (DB422701)
DB972166 (DB433565)
DB972167 (DB432154)
DB972168 (DB423121)
DB972169 (DB427877)
DB972170 (DB423157)
DB972171 (DB425548)
DB972172 (DB431924)
DB972173 (DB426923)
DB972174 (DB428896)
DB972175 (DB422700)
DB972176* (DB429821)
DB972177 (DB426241)
DB972178 (DB433561)
DB972179 (DB423653)
DB972180 (DB427381)
DB972181 (DB427216)
DB972182 (DB433699)
DB972183 (DB429358)
DB972184 (DB433083)
DB972185 (DB425665)
DB972186+ (DB427249)
DB972187 (DB423138)
DB972188 (DB428218)
DB972189 (DB425252)
DB972190 (DB427777)
DB972191 (DB418039)
DB972192= (DB430213)
DB972193 (DB426420)
DB972194 (DB423288)
DB972195 (DB427976)
DB972196+ (DB432919)
DB972197 (DB426935)
DB972198 (DB427448)
DB972199# (DB430300)
DB972200 (DB426427)
DB972201 (DB425842)
DB972202 (DB432436)
DB972203 (DB424809)
DB972204 (DB427878)
DB972205+ (DB431978)
DB972206 (DB423333)
DB972207 (DB424253)
DB972208 (DB423725)
DB972209 (DB423508)
DB972210 (DB425565)
DB972211 (DB429470)
DB972212 (DB423220)
DB972213+ (DB432613)
DB972214 (DB423282)
DB972215 (DB425917)
DB972216 (DB422448)
DB972217 (DB421413)
DB972218 (DB421925)
DB972219 (DB424580)
DB972220+ (DB429725)
DB972221+ (DB433327)
DB972222+ (DB431021)
DB972223+ (DB433471)
DB972224+ (DB433319)
DB972225 (DB428396)
DB972226 (DB415203)
DB972227 (DB418661)
DB972228 (DB416617)
DB972229 (DB427652)
DB972230 (DB422000)
DB972231 (DB431475)
DB972232 (DB426797)
DB972233 (DB427927)
DB972234 (DB423090)
DB972235 (DB427662)
DB972236= (DB429918)
DB972237 (DB422524)
DB972238 (DB425883)
DB972239 (DB424763)
DB972240 (DB433444)
DB972241 (DB422714)
DB972242+ (DB430868)
DB972243 (DB425184)
DB972244 (DB426060)
DB972245+ (DB430978)
DB972246+ (DB431586)
DB972247 (DB428338)
DB972248 (DB426081)
DB972249 (DB427021)
DB972250 (DB423395)
DB972251 (DB427076)
DB972252 (DB418773)
DB972253 (DB423823)
DB972254 (DB427217)
DB972255 (DB424970)
DB972256+ (DB433624)
DB972257 (DB423188)
DB972258 (DB428304)
DB972259+ (DB432265)
DB972260 (DB426880)
DB972261 W(DB424582)
DB972262 (DB428217)
DB972263 (DB421581)
DB972264+ (DB432953)
DB972265 (DB422574)
DB972266 (DB423470)
DB972267 (DB430460)
DB972268 (DB427150)
DB972269 (DB424859)
DB972270 (DB418384)
DB972271 (DB433317)
DB972272 (DB426274)
DB972273 (DB427231)
DB972274 (DB432960)
DB972275+ (DB432297)
DB972276 (DB432725)
DB972277 (DB423065)
DB972278 (DB432785)
DB972279 (DB433588)
DB972280 (DB433066)
DB972281 (DB433016)
DB972282 (DB433528)
DB972283 (DB426283)
DB972284* (DB430624)
DB972285# (DB430112)
DB972286 (DB426907)
DB972287+ (DB431483)
DB972288 (DB426670)
DB972289 (DB426018)
DB972290 (DB425736)
DB972291 (DB418246)
DB972292 (DB433040)
DB972293 (DB431654)
DB972294 (DB429970)
DB972295 (DB427857)
DB972296 (DB425706)
DB972297 (DB423339)
DB972298+ (DB429386)
DB972299 (DB432033)
DB972300* (DB430477)
DB972301 (DB428003)
DB972302 (DB426202)
DB972303 (DB422583)
DB972304 (DB432339)
DB972305 (DB432158)
DB972306 (DB433551)
DB972307 (DB431291)
DB972308 (DB432672)
DB972309 (DB432666)
DB972310 (DB432125)
DB972311 (DB424262)
DB972312+ (DB429634)
DB972313 (DB431450)
DB972314 (DB433467)
DB972315 (DB426821)
DB972316+ (DB433284)
DB972317+ (DB431097)
DB972318 (DB432038)
DB972319 (DB425516)
DB972320 (DB427008)
DB972321 (DB429766)
DB972322 (DB433248)
DB972323 (DB432227)
DB972324# (DB430261)
DB972325 (DB423206)
DB972326 (DB429936)
DB972327+ (DB432287)
DB972328+ (DB433359)
DB972329 (DB426445)
DB972330+ (DB433331)
DB972331+ (DB433636)
DB972332 (DB423223)

DB972333 (DB420171)
DB972334 (DB422742)
DB972335+ (DB430833)
DB972336+ (DB433400)
DB972337 (DB432382)
DB972338 (DB420538)
DB972339 (DB427657)
DB972340 (DB424903)
DB972341 (DB427844)
DB972342 (DB428489)
DB972343 (DB425829)
DB972344+ (DB433438)
DB972345 (DB432343)
DB972346 (DB425547)
DB972347 (DB430196)
DB972348 (DB425043)
DB972349 (DB423279)
DB972350 (DB425143)
DB972351 (DB425203)
DB972352 (DB427093)
DB972353 (DB423494)
DB972354+ (DB431215)
DB972355 (DB425716)
DB972356 (DB432538)
DB972357 (DB424528)
DB972358 (DB425901)
DB972359 (DB420479)
DB972360 (DB420723)
DB972361+ (DB427558)
DB972362 (DB422656)
DB972363 (DB433341)
DB972364 (DB427423)
DB972365 (DB433623)
DB972366 (DB422347)
DB972367 (DB426052)
DB972368 (DB424966)
DB972369 (DB433043)
DB972370 (DB426413)
DB972371 (DB427862)
DB972372 (DB433044)
DB972373 (DB425776)
DB972374+ (DB429740)
DB972375 (DB425837)
DB972376 (DB425664)
DB972377 (DB423851)
DB972378 (DB420561)
DB972379 (DB423200)
DB972380 (DB427439)
DB972381 (DB418869)
DB972382 (DB428442)
DB972383 (DB425598)
DB972384 (DB429606)
DB972385 (DB426665)
DB972386 (DB423852)
DB972387 (DB425136)
DB972388 (DB424944)
DB972389 (DB423601)
DB972390 (DB428359)
DB972391 (DB427975)
DB972392+ (DB432242)
DB972393# (DB430201)
DB972394+ (DB426963)
DB972395 (DB432824)
DB972396 (DB432380)
DB972397+ (DB432457)
DB972398 (DB422577)
DB972399 (DB425821)
DB972400 (DB421440)
DB972401 (DB432674)
DB972402 (DB427061)
DB972403 (DB426860)
DB972404 (DB432858)
DB972405 (DB433041)
DB972406 (DB425853)
DB972407 (DB432604)
DB972408 (DB423656)
DB972409 (DB427692)
DB972410 (DB424338)
DB972411 (DB425798)
DB972412 (DB427513)
DB972413 (DB426500)
DB972414 (DB423850)
DB972415 (DB423086)
DB972416 (DB432511)
DB972417 (DB431245)
DB972418 (DB433747)
DB972419 (DB425642)
DB972420 (DB432400)
DB972421 (DB426561)
DB972422 (DB432520)
DB972423 (DB428627)
DB972424 (DB431908)
DB972425 (DB426299)
DB972426 (DB423887)
DB972427 (DB431241)
DB972428 (DB422739)
DB972429 (DB423403)
DB972430 (DB424634)
DB972431 (DB423212)
DB972432 (DB423501)
DB972433 (DB423932)
DB972434 (DB424312)
DB972435 (DB426937)
DB972436= (DB430686)
DB972437 (DB424605)
DB972438 (DB427634)
DB972439 (DB431554)
DB972440 (DB426361)
DB972441 (DB433053)
DB972442 (DB425619)
DB972443 (DB428274)
DB972444 (DB426634)
DB972445 (DB425629)
DB972446 (DB428615)
DB972447 (DB431310)
DB972448 (DB427527)
DB972449+ (DB429407)
DB972450+ (DB431403)
DB972451+ (DB425846)
DB972452= (DB430431)
DB972453= (DB430678)
DB972454 (DB426544)
DB972455 (DB427042)
DB972456 (DB427933)
DB972457 (DB425990)
DB972458 (DB424358)
DB972459 (DB432229)
DB972460# (DB429869)
DB972461 (DB424300)
DB972462+ (DB432816)
DB972463 (DB419947)
DB972464= (DB430742)
DB972465+ (DB431359)
DB972466 (DB428297)
DB972467 (DB416448)
DB972468 (DB428135)
DB972469 (DB433453)
DB972470 (DB433200)
DB972471 (DB428438)
DB972472+ (DB432447)
DB972473 (DB433568)
DB972474 (DB431575)
DB972475 (DB428809)
DB972476 (DB418679)
DB972477 (DB432680)
DB972478 (DB428470)
DB972479 (DB424996)
DB972480 (DB423892)
DB972481 (DB431828)
DB972482 (DB428014)
DB972483 (DB425845)
DB972484 (DB426429)
DB972485 (DB427185)
DB972486 (DB427390)
DB972487 (DB423743)
DB972488* (DB430694)
DB972489 (DB423544)
DB972490 (DB432456)
DB972491 (DB425846)
DB972492 (DB418728)
DB972493 (DB424392)
DB972494 (DB415629)
DB972495 (DB426706)
DB972496 (DB423856)
DB972497 (DB430887)
DB972498 (DB432705)
DB972499 (DB421788)
DB972500 (DB427705)
DB972501 (DB421333)
DB972502 (DB431580)
DB972503 (DB423355)
DB972504 (DB421374)
DB972505 (DB421488)
DB972506 (DB421318)
DB972507 (DB418095)
DB972508 (DB424465)
DB972509 (DB425044)
DB972510 (DB431845)
DB972511 (DB429662)
DB972512= (DB430553)

DB972513 (DB421521)
DB972514 (DB425832)
DB972515 (DB415601)
DB972516 (DB425135)
DB972517 (DB423106)
DB972518 (DB426416)
DB972519 (DB422487)
DB972520 (DB427400)
DB972521 (DB424921)
DB972522 (DB427952)
DB972523 (DB431373)
DB972524 W(DB429736)
DB972525 (DB427798)
DB972526 (DB427831)
DB972527= (DB430505)
DB972528 (DB431007)
DB972529+ (DB432597)
DB972530 (DB428237)
DB972531 (DB423702)
DB972532 (DB413986)
DB972533+ (DB431369)
DB972534 (DB425339)
DB972535= (DB430260)
DB972536 (DB425410)
DB972537 (DB428098)
DB972538 (DB423119)
DB972539 (DB420690)
DB972540 (DB428015)
DB972541 (DB422674)
DB972542+ (DB431063)
DB972543 (DB430987)
DB972544 (DB429558)
DB972545 (DB423783)
DB972546 (DB424562)
DB972547 (DB423862)
DB972548 (DB425624)
DB972549 (DB432777)
DB972550 (DB429594)
DB972551= (DB429807)
DB972552 (DB431496)
DB972553 (DB426866)
DB972554 (DB431204)
DB972555 (DB429399)
DB972556 (DB431894)
DB972557 (DB432352)
DB972558 (DB433457)
DB972559* (DB429956)
DB972560 (DB422588)
DB972561 (DB432570)
DB972562 (DB432117)
DB972563 (DB433074)
DB972564 (DB427515)
DB972565 (DB428055)
DB972566+ (DB431469)
DB972567 (DB433519)
DB972568 (DB425976)
DB972569 (DB420312)
DB972570+ (DB433746)
DB972571 (DB427597)
DB972572+ (DB431944)
DB972573= (DB430608)
DB972574+ (DB429615)
DB972575+ (DB429373)
DB972576 (DB423498)
DB972577 (DB427506)
DB972578 (DB424210)
DB972579 (DB423315)
DB972580 (DB420220)
DB972581 (DB430680)
DB972582 (DB423221)
DB972583+ (DB432985)
DB972584 (DB423305)
DB972585 (DB431335)
DB972586 (DB426207)
DB972587 (DB424931)
DB972588 (DB427333)
DB972589 (DB420012)
DB972590 (DB425534)
DB972591 (DB427521)
DB972592 (DB427863)
DB972593 (DB426962)
DB972594= (DB430208)
DB972595 (DB425778)
DB972596 (DB433361)
DB972597 (DB426035)
DB972598 (DB427791)
DB972599+ (DB431577)
DB972600+ (DB429459)
DB972601# (DB430205)
DB972602 (DB424366)
DB972603 (DB420423)
DB972604 (DB426933)
DB972605+ (DB430835)
DB972606 (DB419283)
DB972607+ (DB431549)
DB972608+ (DB429763)
DB972609+ (DB430864)
DB972610 (DB428262)
DB972611# (DB429813)
DB972612# (DB430764)
DB972613# (DB429837)
DB972614+ (DB431787)
DB972615 (DB432998)
DB972616 (DB423322)
DB972617 (DB425684)
DB972618 (DB426311)
DB972619+ (DB433324)
DB972620 (DB423699)
DB972621 (DB425630)
DB972622 (DB431508)
DB972623 (DB416720)
DB972624 (DB428276)
DB972625 (DB423844)
DB972626+ (DB432867)
DB972627+ (DB433718)
DB972628 (DB424551)
DB972629 (DB426120)
DB972630 (DB423785)
DB972631 (DB415150)
DB972632 (DB432413)
DB972633= (DB430598)
DB972634 (DB419435)
DB972635 (DB428225)
DB972636 (DB428167)
DB972637+ (DB432221)
DB972638 (DB427769)
DB972639+ (DB431011)
DB972640 (DB430564)
DB972641 (DB425701)
DB972642 (DB432282)
DB972643= (DB430718)
DB972644 (DB423941)
DB972645 (DB423712)
DB972646 (DB426438)
DB972647 (DB427745)
DB972648 (DB423291)
DB972649 (DB426959)
DB972650 (DB426161)
DB972651 (DB427039)
DB972652 (DB427555)
DB972653 (DB426742)
DB972654 (DB424609)
DB972655 (DB428479)
DB972656+ (DB432105)
DB972657 (DB424352)
DB972658 (DB431268)
DB972659 (DB419985)
DB972660 (DB426844)
DB972661 (DB425782)
DB972662* (DB429962)
DB972663 (DB426458)
DB972664* (DB430319)
DB972665= (DB430100)
DB972666 (DB427765)
DB972667 (DB425557)
DB972668 (DB431172)
DB972669 (DB432494)
DB972670 (DB422589)
DB972671 (DB428177)
DB972672 (DB430922)
DB972673 (DB416167)
DB972674 (DB425189)
DB972675 (DB432738)
DB972676= (DB430650)
DB972677= (DB430362)
DB972678 (DB424621)
DB972679 (DB432754)
DB972680 (DB431126)
DB972681 (DB424802)
DB972682 (DB426257)
DB972683 (DB431962)
DB972684 (DB418683)
DB972685 (DB423252)
DB972686 (DB427739)
DB972687= (DB430503)
DB972688 (DB423151)
DB972689# (DB430015)
DB972690 (DB432779)
DB972691 (DB423918)
DB972692 (DB423424)

DB972693 (DB423540)
DB972694+ (DB430822)
DB972695 (DB426467)
DB972696 (DB427668)
DB972697 (DB424532)
DB972698 (DB424254)
DB972699 (DB426711)
DB972700+ (DB432932)
DB972701 (DB425961)
DB972702 (DB428096)
DB972703 (DB433125)
DB972704+ (DB429726)
DB972705 (DB426938)
DB972706 (DB427747)
DB972707 (DB425652)
DB972708 (DB418137)
DB972709 (DB424412)
DB972710 (DB428012)
DB972711 (DB424316)
DB972712 (DB423598)
DB972713 (DB433376)
DB972714= (DB430749)
DB972715 (DB426109)
DB972716 (DB423551)
DB972717 (DB427268)
DB972718 (DB419655)
DB972719 (DB427700)
DB972720 (DB425112)
DB972721 (DB424320)
DB972722 (DB426814)
DB972723 (DB425069)
DB972724 (DB426121)
DB972725 (DB432569)
DB972726 (DB432753)
DB972727 (DB426297)
DB972728 (DB423908)
DB972729 (DB426971)
DB972730 (DB428220)
DB972731 (DB427497)
DB972732 (DB418758)
DB972733 (DB418441)
DB972734 (DB427629)
DB972735 (DB427825)
DB972736 (DB432762)
DB972737 (DB426140)
DB972738 (DB423452)
DB972739+ (DB432362)
DB972740 (DB424920)
DB972741 (DB427202)
DB972742 (DB426230)
DB972743 (DB423380)
DB972744 (DB426904)
DB972745+ (DB431289)
DB972746 (DB428651)
DB972747 (DB424844)
DB972748 (DB425483)
DB972749 (DB424405)
DB972750 (DB427926)
DB972751= (DB429976)
DB972752 (DB427842)
DB972753 (DB424205)
DB972754 (DB425142)
DB972755 (DB427537)
DB972756 (DB427790)
DB972757 (DB427479)
DB972758 (DB423062)
DB972759 (DB421977)
DB972760 (DB430894)
DB972761 (DB422735)
DB972762 (DB431270)
DB972763 (DB428063)
DB972764 (DB425987)
DB972765 (DB426302)
DB972766 (DB432653)
DB972767 (DB422602)
DB972768 (DB428428)
DB972769 (DB417921)
DB972770 (DB425265)
DB972771= (DB430391)
DB972772 (DB425432)
DB972773 (DB423381)
DB972774 (DB425737)
DB972775 (DB428017)
DB972776 (DB425873)
DB972777 (DB423218)
DB972778 (DB423929)
DB972779 (DB425648)
DB972780 (DB429536)
DB972781 (DB423566)
DB972782 (DB428636)
DB972783 (DB426566)
DB972784 (DB340893)
DB972785 (DB426791)
DB972786 (DB426184)
DB972787 (DB427835)
DB972788 (DB419551)
DB972789+ (DB433387)
DB972790 (DB427711)
DB972791* (DB428368)
DB972792 (DB427683)
DB972793 (DB422566)
DB972794+ (DB428518)
DB972795+ (DB433533)
DB972796 (DB427378)
DB972797 (DB428846)
DB972798 (DB423435)
DB972799 (DB424251)

Number Series: DB973000 - DB973449

Description: 21T Ballast Sleeper Wagon
Builder: RFS Doncaster
Powell Duffryn
Converted: 1989-90
Tare Weight: 10.3t * 10.4t 10.6t +
G.L.W.: 32.0t
Design Code: ZC006A ZC006B * ZC007A + ZC009A = ZC009B #
Tops Code: ZCV
Fishkind: "CLAM"

DB973000 (DB433035)
DB973001 (DB425467)
DB973002+ (DB431624)
DB973003 (DB424331)
DB973004 (DB423524)
DB973005 (DB425655)
DB973006+ (DB432755)
DB973007 (DB423128)
DB973008 (DB433466)
DB973009 (DB425541)
DB973010 (DB415838)
DB973011 (DB430972)
DB973012 (DB432729)
DB973013 (DB428325)
DB973014* (DB430292)
DB973015 (DB420294)
DB973016 (DB421081)
DB973017 (DB421484)
DB973018 (DB423952)
DB973019 (DB424403)
DB973020 (DB424434)
DB973021 (DB432845)
DB973022 (DB425788)
DB973023 (DB429372)
DB973024 (DB427155)
DB973025 (DB425691)
DB973026 (DB432700)
DB973027 (DB433634)
DB973028 (DB431086)
DB973029 (DB426227)
DB973030 (DB432160)
DB973031 (DB423731)
DB973032 (DB427237)
DB973033 (DB432965)
DB973034 (DB427243)
DB973035 (DB426660)

DB973036 (DB427716)
DB973037 (DB426323)
DB973038 (DB431468)
DB973039 (DB426368)
DB973040 (DB420116)
DB973041 (DB423349)
DB973042 (DB425207)
DB973043 (DB427509)
DB973044 (DB426740)
DB973045* (DB430149)
DB973046 (DB432841)
DB973047 (DB425709)
DB973048 (DB427694)
DB973049 (DB427189)
DB973050 (DB423255)
DB973051 (DB422732)
DB973052 (DB433388)
DB973053 (DB426019)
DB973054 (DB432304)
DB973055 (DB428994)
DB973056 (DB427252)
DB973057 (DB432163)
DB973058 (DB430630)
DB973059 (DB429656)
DB973060 (DB432840)
DB973061 (DB427315)
DB973062 (DB433537)
DB973063 (DB427177)
DB973064 (DB423503)
DB973065 (DB432452)
DB973066 (DB432582)
DB973067 (DB432031)
DB973068 (DB423091)
DB973069 (DB426664)
DB973070 (DB427789)
DB973071 (DB422636)
DB973072 (DB428638)
DB973073 (DB431826)
DB973074 (DB425774)
DB973075 (DB424476)
DB973076 (DB426064)
DB973077+ (DB431024)
DB973078 (DB419438)
DB973079 (DB433193)
DB973080 (DB425810)
DB973081 (DB420222)
DB973082 (DB426387)
DB973083 (DB426492)
DB973084 (DB432037)
DB973085+ (DB431031)
DB973086 (DB432519)
DB973087 (DB426041)
DB973088 (DB427621)
DB973089 (DB427901)
DB973090 (DB433433)
DB973091 (DB431993)
DB973092 (DB427661)
DB973093 (DB426941)
DB973094 (DB424415)
DB973095 (DB427068)
DB973096 (DB427663)
DB973097 (DB423485)
DB973098 (DB423713)
DB973099 (DB431453)
DB973100 (DB423346)
DB973101 (DB425897)
DB973102# (DB430648)
DB973103 (DB432763)
DB973104 (DB432399)
DB973105 (DB429657)
DB973106 (DB422028)
DB973107+ (DB431637)
DB973108 (DB429643)
DB973109 (DB424330)
DB973110 (DB427535)
DB973111 (DB430837)
DB973112 (DB423441)
DB973113 (DB422511)
DB973114 (DB427483)
DB973115+ (DB427171)
DB973116 (DB424951)
DB973117 (DB418167)
DB973118 (DB425772)
DB973119 (DB420498)
DB973120 (DB428663)
DB973121 (DB432992)
DB973122+ (DB431255)
DB973123* (DB430471)
DB973124 (DB427514)
DB973125 (DB420874)
DB973126 (DB431458)
DB973127 (DB420827)
DB973128 (DB426819)
DB973129 (DB422711)
DB973130 (DB423304)
DB973131 (DB428371)
DB973132 (DB425401)
DB973133+ (DB433084)
DB973134 (DB427345)
DB973135 (DB433515)
DB973136# (DB429810)
DB973137 (DB432000)
DB973138+ (DB431590)
DB973139 (DB432575)
DB973140 (DB425293)
DB973141 (DB426921)
DB973142 (DB422743)
DB973143 (DB427256)
DB973144 (DB432267)
DB973145 (DB426826)
DB973146+ (DB430951)
DB973147 (DB422139)
DB973148* (DB430313)
DB973149+ (DB431731)
DB973150 (DB430962)
DB973151 (DB423467)
DB973152= (DB430311)
DB973153 (DB423686)
DB973154= (DB429885)
DB973155 (DB427296)
DB973156 (DB425610)
DB973157 (DB427859)
DB973158 (DB425848)
DB973159 (DB423675)
DB973160 (DB425080)
DB973161 (DB420579)
DB973162 (DB426597)
DB973163+ (DB431072)
DB973164+ (DB433064)
DB973165+ (DB430999)
DB973166 (DB420732)
DB973167+ (DB433032)
DB973168 (DB423078)
DB973169= (DB430301)
DB973170 (DB427499)
DB973171 (DB423756)
DB973172 (DB423751)
DB973173 (DB420844)
DB973174 (DB424510)
DB973175 (DB425078)
DB973176+ (DB425602)
DB973177 (DB426158)
DB973178 (DB426090)
DB973179 (DB425567)
DB973180 (DB426245)
DB973181 (DB432668)
DB973182 (DB427776)
DB973183+ (DB431877)
DB973184+ (DB431436)
DB973185= (DB429842)
DB973186 (DB427677)
DB973187+ (DB432462)
DB973188+ (DB433046)
DB973189+ (DB431966)
DB973190+ (DB431893)
DB973191+ (DB431844)
DB973192 (DB429504)
DB973193 (DB426239)
DB973194 (DB426888)
DB973195 (DB428016)
DB973196 (DB425572)
DB973197 (DB427168)
DB973198 (DB424351)
DB973199 (DB426011)
DB973200 (DB427122)
DB973201 (DB421796)
DB973202 (DB424439)
DB973203 (DB432908)
DB973204 (DB433443)
DB973205* (DB430399)
DB973206 (DB433460)
DB973207 (DB433507)
DB973208* (DB430737)
DB973209* (DB430576)
DB973210 (DB422480)
DB973211 (DB416076)
DB973212 (DB422653)
DB973213 (DB433103)
DB973214+ (DB432967)
DB973215 (DB424461)

DB973216+ (DB431885)
DB973217 (DB423081)
DB973218 (DB429044)
DB973219 (DB433363)
DB973220 (DB418463)
DB973221 (DB432553)
DB973222 (DB418805)
DB973223 (DB423868)
DB973224 (DB428917)
DB973225+ (DB431967)
DB973226 (DB433179)
DB973227 (DB426392)
DB973228 (DB433013)
DB973229 (DB423768)
DB973230 (DB423236)
DB973231 (DB432096)
DB973232 (DB427614)
DB973233 (DB426129)
DB973234 (DB424390)
DB973235 (DB425843)
DB973236 (DB426156)
DB973237 (DB422637)
DB973238 (DB433153)
DB973239 (DB430701)
DB973240+ (DB431596)
DB973241* (DB430509)
DB973242 (DB424277)
DB973243 (DB426330)
DB973244 (DB423645)
DB973245 (DB423814)
DB973246 (DB423644)
DB973247 (DB428239)
DB973248 (DB425352)
DB973249 (DB428324)
DB973250+ (DB431737)
DB973251+ (DB427785)
DB973252+ (DB433673)
DB973253= (DB430522)
DB973254= (DB430708)
DB973255 (DB428068)
DB973256= (DB430089)
DB973257 (DB433071)
DB973258* (DB430026)
DB973259= (DB430768)
DB973260 (DB426141)
DB973261 (DB432922)
DB973262+ (DB431883)
DB973263= (DB430170)
DB973264+ (DB429499)
DB973265 (DB427587)
DB973266 (DB421762)
DB973267 (DB426432)
DB973268 (DB428140)
DB973269 (DB423509)
DB973270+ (DB430956)
DB973271 (DB424550)
DB973272+ (DB432323)
DB973273 (DB423070)
DB973274+ (DB431339)
DB973275 (DB427829)
DB973276 (DB422616)
DB973277+ (DB430801)
DB973278+ (DB427038)
DB973279+ (DB431495)
DB973280+ (DB431427)
DB973281 (DB427910)
DB973282 (DB433708)
DB973283 (DB433051)
DB973284 (DB425785)
DB973285 (DB423360)
DB973286 (DB422556)
DB973287+ (DB429422)
DB973288+ (DB432543)
DB973289* (DB430500)
DB973290 (DB425646)
DB973291* (DB430405)
DB973292 (DB423455)
DB973293 (DB432381)
DB973294 (DB425904)
DB973295 (DB419867)
DB973296 (DB421479)
DB973297 (DB428497)
DB973298 (DB426442)
DB973299 (DB423525)
DB973300* (DB430180)
DB973301 (DB424529)
DB973302+ (DB420792)
DB973303+ (DB340899)
DB973304 (DB423705)
DB973305 (DB421444)
DB973306 (DB432261)
DB973307 (DB422584)
DB973308 (DB426788)
DB973309 (DB427899)
DB973310 (DB425072)
DB973311 (DB431356)
DB973312 (DB431786)
DB973313 (DB425501)
DB973314 (DB431385)
DB973315 (DB431988)
DB973316 (DB415582)
DB973317 (DB424429)
DB973318 (DB431506)
DB973319 (DB427182)
DB973320 (DB429379)
DB973321* (DB430346)
DB973322 (DB422621)
DB973323 (DB423132)
DB973324 (DB424659)
DB973325* (DB430497)
DB973326+ (DB431388)
DB973327= (DB430588)
DB973328 (DB423488)
DB973329 (DB426084)
DB973330 (DB425909)
DB973331 (DB427317)
DB973332 (DB422614)
DB973333 (DB423721)
DB973334 (DB429650)
DB973335+ (DB432843)
DB973336+ (DB429350)
DB973337 (DB433000)
DB973338= (DB430051)
DB973339 (DB421636)
DB973340 (DB425013)
DB973341* (DB430443)
DB973342 (DB427223)
DB973343 (DB426900)
DB973344 (DB433099)
DB973345 (DB423421)
DB973346 (DB423222)
DB973347 (DB425601)
DB973348 (DB428447)
DB973349 (DB422601)
DB973350 (DB426306)
DB973351 (DB432720)
DB973352 (DB427956)
DB973353 (DB422412)
DB973354 (DB422365)
DB973355 (DB433424)
DB973356 (DB422364)
DB973357* (DB430009)
DB973358 (DB426517)
DB973359* (DB430511)
DB973360 (DB433008)
DB973361 (DB432826)
DB973362 (DB425403)
DB973363 (DB427417)
DB973364 (DB422311)
DB973365 (DB423051)
DB973366 (DB429685)
DB973367 (DB419181)
DB973368 (DB432928)
DB973369 (DB432416)
DB973370 (DB425046)
DB973371 (DB432464)
DB973372 (DB423067)
DB973373 (DB427160)
DB973374 (DB423399)
DB973375 (DB425409)
DB973376 (DB427484)
DB973377 (DB433581)
DB973378 (DB429463)
DB973379 (DB423939)
DB973380 (DB433354)
DB973381 (DB423627)
DB973382 (DB424823)
DB973383 (DB423537)
DB973384 (DB431340)
DB973385 (DB426641)
DB973386 (DB419923)
DB973387 (DB431593)
DB973388 (DB423270)
DB973389 (DB426809)
DB973390 (DB425546)
DB973391+ (DB430810)
DB973392 (DB428496)
DB973393+ (DB429369)
DB973394 (DB426586)
DB973395 (DB432778)

DB973396	(DB432957)	DB973414	(DB425559)	DB973432	(DB427699)
DB973397	(DB425992)	DB973415	(DB429731)	DB973433	(DB425780)
DB973398	(DB423411)	DB973416	(DB432182)	DB973434	(DB426668)
DB973399	(DB425643)	DB973417	(DB430539)	DB973435	(DB430748)
DB973400	(DB425738)	DB973418	(DB431876)	DB973436	(DB430780)
DB973401	(DB425526)	DB973419	(DB425678)	DB973437	(DB425626)
DB973402	(DB423372)	DB973420	(DB425696)	DB973438	(DB433140)
DB973403	(DB423502)	DB973421	(DB428152)	DB973439	(DB425429)
DB973404	(DB424546)	DB973422	(DB433247)	DB973440	(DB425951)
DB973405	(DB422673)	DB973423	(DB430860)	DB973441	(DB433583)
DB973406	(DB420496)	DB973424	(DB423622)	DB973442	(DB430017)
DB973407	(DB427658)	DB973425	(DB422567)	DB973443	(DB430612)
DB973408	(DB427459)	DB973426	(DB424342)	DB973444	(DB432944)
DB973409	(DB423857)	DB973427	(DB428179)	DB973445	(DB427766)
DB973410	(DB425304)	DB973428	(DB433441)	DB973446	(DB425922)
DB973411	(DB423251)	DB973429	(DB427372)	DB973447	(DB433022)
DB973412	(DB428282)	DB973430	(DB423313)	DB973448	(DB423077)
DB973413	(DB425517)	DB973431	(DB423513)	DB973449	(DB432081)

Number Series: ADB976016 - ADB976027

Description: Bogie Cable Drum Carrier
Builder: BR (Stewarts Lane C & W)
Tare Weight: 17.5t 37.5t +
Design Code: YV503B YV504A +

Lot No.: 3780
Converted: 1971
G.L.W.: 38.0t 78.0t +
Tops Code: YVP

ADB976016+
ADB976017 (W)
ADB976018
ADB976019
ADB976020
ADB976021
ADB976022
ADB976023
ADB976024
ADB976025
ADB976026
ADB976027

Number Series: ADB976040

Description: Match Wagon
Builder: BR (Swindon Works)
Tare Weight: 20.5t
Design Code: ZX105D

Lot No.: 3796
Converted: 1973
G.L.W.: 20.5t
Tops Code: ZXR

ADB976040 (W)

Number Series: ADB976042

Description: Match Wagon
Builder: BR (Horwich Works)
Tare Weight: 8.0t
Design Code: YX024A

Lot No.: 3808
Converted: 1973
G.L.W.: 18.0t
Tops Code: ZXV

ADB976042

Number Series: DB978000 - DB978991

Description: 34T Bogie Ballast Wagon
Builder: BR (Shildon Works)
BR (Swindon Works)
RFS Doncaster
Tare Weight: 14.0t
Design Code: YC502A YC502C * YX072A =
Fishkind: "TURBOT" "HERON" *

Lot No.: 4021
Built: 1982-88
G.L.W.: 48.0t
Tops Code: YCV YXW =

DB978000 (DB924285)
DB978001 (DB923736)
DB978002 (DB923785)
DB978003 ( )
DB978005 (DB924065)
DB978006 (DB923606)
DB978007 (DB924876)
DB978008 (DB924354)
DB978009 (DB924032)
DB978010 (DB923682)
DB978011 (DB924215)
DB978012 (DB923419)
DB978013 (DB924855)
DB978016 (DB924013)
DB978017 (DB924130)
DB978018 (DB923979)
DB978019 (DB923713)
DB978020 (DB924887)
DB978021 (DB923831)
DB978022 (DB923967)
DB978023 (DB923688)
DB978024 (DB923558)
DB978025 (DB923861)
DB978026 (DB923440)
DB978027 (DB923459)
DB978028 (DB923958)
DB978029 (DB924140)
DB978030 (DB923398)
DB978032 (DB923512)
DB978033 (DB924200)
DB978034 W(DB923756)
DB978035 (DB923395)
DB978036 (DB923939)
DB978037 (DB923836)
DB978038 (DB923640)
DB978040 (DB923529)
DB978042 (DB924327)
DB978045 (DB923562)
DB978046 (DB923429)
DB978047 (DB924846)
DB978048 (DB924213)
DB978049 W(DB923871)
DB978050 W(DB923561)
DB978051 (DB923578)
DB978053 (DB923972)
DB978054 (DB924357)
DB978055 (DB923369)
DB978056 W(DB924866)
DB978057 (DB923784)
DB978058 (DB923540)
DB978060 (DB924066)
DB978061 (DB923726)
DB978062 (DB923891)
DB978063 W(DB923681)
DB978064 (DB923688)
DB978065 (DB923635)
DB978066 (DB923886)
DB978067 (DB923709)
DB978068* (DB924379)
DB978069 (DB924355)
DB978070 (DB923472)
DB978071 (DB924019)
DB978073 W(DB923659)
DB978075 (DB923589)
DB978076 (DB924010)
DB978077 (DB923391)
DB978078 (DB923505)
DB978079 (DB923521)
DB978080 (DB924090)
DB978082 (DB923665)
DB978084 (DB924350)
DB978085 (DB924238)
DB978086 (DB923971)
DB978087 (DB924050)
DB978088 (DB924288)
DB978089 (DB924821)
DB978090 (DB923719)
DB978091 (DB923600)
DB978092 (DB923514)
DB978093 (DB923881)
DB978094 (DB923858)
DB978095 (DB923573)
DB978096 (DB924134)
DB978097 (DB924195)
DB978099 (DB923423)
DB978102 (DB924248)
DB978103 (DB924333)
DB978104 (DB923620)
DB978105 (DB923673)
DB978106 (DB923330)
DB978107 (DB923324)
DB978108 (DB923447)
DB978109 (DB923945)
DB978114 (DB923705)
DB978115 W(DB923829)
DB978116 W(DB923716)
DB978118 (DB923979)
DB978119 (DB923713)
DB978120 (DB924887)
DB978121 (DB923831)
DB978122 W(DB923967)
DB978123 W(DB924235)
DB978125 (DB923905)
DB978126 (DB923448)
DB978127 W(DB923752)
DB978132 W(DB923328)
DB978133 W(DB923638)
DB978138 (DB923889)
DB978139 (DB923517)
DB978140 (DB924041)
DB978143 (DB923739)
DB978145 (DB923399)
DB978146 (DB923654)
DB978147 W(DB923496)
DB978151 W(DB923696)
DB978155 W(DB923897)
DB978156 (DB924083)
DB978157 (DB923894)
DB978158 (DB924017)
DB978159 (DB924814)
DB978160 (DB924057)
DB978161 (DB924103)
DB978162 (DB923629)
DB978163 (DB923974)
DB978164 (DB924064)
DB978165 (DB923699)
DB978166 (DB923641)
DB978167 (DB923842)
DB978168 (DB923751)
DB978169 W(DB923588)
DB978170 (DB924804)
DB978171 (DB924272)
DB978175 (DB923684)
DB978176 (DB924099)
DB978178 (DB923952)
DB978182 W(DB924067)
DB978183 (DB923810)
DB978185 (DB924164)
DB978186 (DB924322)
DB978187 (DB924294)
DB978190 (DB923839)
DB978191 (DB923970)
DB978192 (DB923487)
DB978194 (DB923424)
DB978195 (DB924312)
DB978197 (DB924261)
DB978200 (DB924061)
DB978201 (DB923980)
DB978202 (DB923594)
DB978203 (DB923995)

DB978205 (DB924226)
DB978206 (DB923888)
DB978209 (DB923410)
DB978210 (DB923754)
DB978211 (DB923802)
DB978212 (DB923691)
DB978214 (DB923893)
DB978215 (DB924242)
DB978216 (DB923593)
DB978217 (DB924110)
DB978218 (DB923976)
DB978219 (DB924228)
DB978221 (DB923509)
DB978222 (DB924896)
DB978224 (DB924302)
DB978225 (DB924016)
DB978235 (DB924202)
DB978236 (DB924038)
DB978238 W(DB924035)
DB978242 (DB923351)
DB978243 W(DB923957)
DB978246 (DB923356)
DB978248 W(DB924222)
DB978249 (DB923782)
DB978251 (DB923446)
DB978253 (DB923767)
DB978254 (DB923522)
DB978255 (DB923357)
DB978256 (DB923427)
DB978258 (DB924865)
DB978259 (DB923494)
DB978260 (DB923618)
DB978261 (DB924240)
DB978262 (DB923327)
DB978263 (DB923956)
DB978264 (DB924219)
DB978265 (DB924873)
DB978266 (DB924190)
DB978267* (DB924881)
DB978268 (DB923502)
DB978269 (DB923818)
DB978270 (DB923456)
DB978271 (DB923630)
DB978272 (DB924243)
DB978273 (DB923349)
DB978274 (DB924006)
DB978275 (DB923307)
DB978276 (DB924111)
DB978277 (DB924872)
DB978278 (DB924286)
DB978279 (DB923738)
DB978280 (DB923679)
DB978281 (DB923613)
DB978282 (DB923371)
DB978283 (DB923366)
DB978284 (DB924204)
DB978285 (DB924863)
DB978286 (DB923656)
DB978287 (DB923789)
DB978288 (DB924123)
DB978289 W(DB923847)
DB978290 (DB924297)
DB978291 (DB924335)
DB978292 (DB923702)
DB978293 (DB923412)
DB978294 (DB923535)
DB978295 (DB923586)
DB978296 (DB924156)
DB978297 (DB924293)
DB978298 (DB923777)
DB978299 (DB923375)
DB978300 (DB923643)
DB978301 (DB923824)
DB978302 (DB923722)
DB978303 (DB924188)
DB978304 (DB923300)
DB978305 (DB924815)
DB978306 (DB923693)
DB978307 (DB923343)
DB978308 (DB923418)
DB978310 (DB924346)
DB978312 (DB924135)
DB978313 (DB923697)
DB978314 (DB923651)
DB978315 (DB923904)
DB978316 (DB923511)
DB978317 (DB923910)
DB978318 (DB923740)
DB978319 (DB924880)
DB978320 (DB923441)
DB978321 (DB923605)
DB978322 (DB923386)
DB978323 (DB924117)
DB978324 (DB924295)
DB978325 (DB923664)
DB978326 (DB923922)
DB978327 (DB923677)
DB978328 (DB924124)
DB978329 (DB923809)
DB978330 (DB923814)
DB978331 (DB923501)
DB978332 (DB924072)
DB978333 (DB924879)
DB978334 (DB923761)
DB978335 (DB923402)
DB978336 (DB923637)
DB978337 W(DB923770)
DB978338 (DB923915)
DB978339 (DB923473)
DB978340 (DB923723)
DB978341 (DB923874)
DB978342 (DB923822)
DB978343 (DB924829)
DB978344 (DB924375)
DB978345 W(DB924840)
DB978346 (DB923780)
DB978347 (DB924160)
DB978348 (DB924157)
DB978350 (DB923938)
DB978351 (DB924227)
DB978352 (DB924199)
DB978353 W(DB924886)
DB978354 (DB923658)
DB978355 (DB923678)
DB978356 (DB923680)
DB978357 (DB924314)
DB978358 (DB924133)
DB978359 (DB923943)
DB978360 (DB923568)
DB978361 (DB924030)
DB978362 (DB924079)
DB978363 W(DB924889)
DB978364 (DB924301)
DB978365 (DB924842)
DB978366 (DB923917)
DB978367 (DB923717)
DB978368 (DB924318)
DB978369 (DB923421)
DB978372 (DB923623)
DB978373 (DB924852)
DB978376 (DB923334)
DB978377 (DB923547)
DB978379 (DB923336)
DB978380 (DB924313)
DB978381* (DB924246)
DB978382 (DB924277)
DB978383 (DB924834)
DB978384 (DB923755)
DB978389 (DB923374)
DB978391 (DB923660)
DB978392 (DB923989)
DB978393 (DB924838)
DB978394 (DB924004)
DB978395 (DB923582)
DB978396 (DB923955)
DB978397 (DB923687)
DB978398 (DB923388)
DB978400 W(DB924269)
DB978401 (DB923807)
DB978402 (DB923564)
DB978403 W(DB923772)
DB978404 W(DB923639)
DB978407 W(DB923590)
DB978408 (DB924167)
DB978409 (DB923675)
DB978410 W(DB924306)
DB978411 (DB924869)
DB978412 (DB924328)
DB978413 (DB924311)
DB978414 W(DB924384)
DB978415 (DB923763)
DB978417 (DB923823)
DB978418 (DB923532)
DB978419 (DB924206)
DB978420 (DB923625)
DB978425 (DB923927)
DB978426 (DB923491)
DB978428 (DB924351)
DB978429 (DB923322)
DB978430 (DB924185)

DB978431 (DB924883)
DB978432 (DB924154)
DB978433 (DB924854)
DB978434 (DB924370)
DB978435 (DB924895)
DB978436 (DB923332)
DB978437 (DB924806)
DB978438 W(DB924250)
DB978439 W(DB923601)
DB978440 (DB923803)
DB978441 W(DB923999)
DB978442 (DB924208)
DB978443 (DB924862)
DB978445 (DB924816)
DB978446 (DB923571)
DB978447 (DB924063)
DB978448 (DB923990)
DB978449 (DB923520)
DB978450 (DB923304)
DB978453 (DB924296)
DB978454 (DB923817)
DB978460 (DB923471)
DB978461 (DB923422)
DB978464 (DB923832)
DB978465 (DB923407)
DB978466 (DB924284)
DB978469 W(DB923576)
DB978471 (DB923339)
DB978473 (DB923409)
DB978474 (DB923352)
DB978475 (DB923435)
DB978476 (DB924040)
DB978477 (DB923508)
DB978478 (DB924197)
DB978479 (DB924817)
DB978480 W(DB923791)
DB978481 (DB924321)
DB978482 (DB924056)
DB978483 (DB923507)
DB978484 W(DB923396)
DB978485 (DB923467)
DB978486 (DB923724)
DB978487 (DB923937)
DB978488 (DB923868)
DB978489 (DB923428)
DB978490 (DB923959)
DB978491 (DB924096)
DB978492 (DB923486)
DB978493 (DB924276)
DB978494 (DB923860)
DB978495 (DB924171)
DB978496 (DB924143)
DB978497 (DB923519)
DB978498 (DB923475)
DB978499 (DB924179)
DB978500 (DB923737)
DB978501 (DB923312)
DB978502 (DB923626)
DB978503 (DB923633)
DB978504 (DB923988)
DB978505 (DB923302)
DB978506 (DB924239)
DB978507 (DB923646)
DB978508 (DB923788)
DB978509 (DB923746)
DB978510 (DB923828)
DB978511 (DB923733)
DB978512 (DB923570)
DB978513 (DB923804)
DB978514 (DB924191)
DB978515 (DB924115)
DB978516 (DB923592)
DB978517 (DB923919)
DB978518 (DB923834)
DB978519 (DB923316)
DB978520 (DB923354)
DB978521 (DB924394)
DB978522 (DB924027)
DB978523 (DB924844)
DB978524 (DB924324)
DB978525 (DB923450)
DB978526 (DB924058)
DB978527 (DB924118)
DB978528 (DB923879)
DB978529* (DB923342)
DB978530 (DB923627)
DB978532 (DB924332)
DB978533 (DB923430)
DB978534 (DB923953)
DB978535 (DB924315)
DB978536 (DB924127)
DB978537 (DB923727)
DB978538 (DB923321)
DB978539 (DB923878)
DB978540 (DB923916)
DB978541 (DB923389)
DB978542 (DB924074)
DB978543 (DB923774)
DB978544 (DB924356)
DB978545 (DB924836)
DB978546 (DB923963)
DB978547 (DB923721)
DB978548 (DB924149)
DB978549 (DB923531)
DB978550 (DB923577)
DB978551 W(DB923549)
DB978552 (DB924223)
DB978553 (DB923983)
DB978554 (DB924125)
DB978555 (DB924850)
DB978556 (DB924192)
DB978557 (DB923303)
DB978558 (DB924182)
DB978559 (DB923543)
DB978560 (DB923539)
DB978561 (DB923337)
DB978562 (DB923830)
DB978563 (DB923837)
DB978564 (DB923438)
DB978565 (DB923709)
DB978566 (DB924187)
DB978567 (DB924278)
DB978568 (DB924060)
DB978569 (DB924018)
DB978570 (DB923864)
DB978571 (DB924054)
DB978572 (DB923560)
DB978573 (DB923920)
DB978574 (DB924011)
DB978575 (DB923554)
DB978576 (DB923348)
DB978577 (DB923363)
DB978578 (DB923310)
DB978579 (DB924281)
DB978580 (DB923931)
DB978581 (DB923765)
DB978582 (DB923729)
DB978583 (DB923434)
DB978584 (DB924329)
DB978585 (DB923911)
DB978586 (DB924009)
DB978587 (DB924376)
DB978588 (DB923872)
DB978589 (DB924885)
DB978590 (DB923750)
DB978591 (DB924234)
DB978592 (DB923711)
DB978593 (DB923666)
DB978594 (DB923918)
DB978595 (DB924352)
DB978596 (DB923492)
DB978597 (DB923527)
DB978598 (DB923479)
DB978599 (DB923484)
DB978601 (DB923985)
DB978602 (DB923848)
DB978603 (DB924028)
DB978604 (DB923901)
DB978605 (DB923397)
DB978606 (DB923436)
DB978607 (DB924273)
DB978608 (DB923404)
DB978609 (DB923820)
DB978611 (DB923865)
DB978612 (DB924212)
DB978613 (DB924833)
DB978614 (DB924047)
DB978615 (DB923982)
DB978616 (DB923766)
DB978617 (DB923793)
DB978619 (DB923379)
DB978620 (DB924144)
DB978621 (DB923377)
DB978622 (DB924159)
DB978623 (DB924898)
DB978624 (DB924205)
DB978625 (DB924381)
DB978626 (DB923757)
DB978627 (DB923461)
DB978628 (DB923546)

DB978629 (DB924150)
DB978630 (DB924113)
DB978631 (DB924801)
DB978632 (DB923445)
DB978633 (DB923550)
DB978635 (DB924340)
DB978636 (DB924229)
DB978637 (DB924059)
DB978638 (DB924005)
DB978639 (DB923541)
DB978640 (DB924001)
DB978641 (DB924851)
DB978643 (DB923325)
DB978644 (DB923951)
DB978645 (DB924811)
DB978646 (DB924015)
DB978647 (DB924078)
DB978648 (DB923462)
DB978649 (DB924894)
DB978650 (DB924309)
DB978651 (DB923460)
DB978652 (DB923747)
DB978653 (DB924153)
DB978654 (DB923311)
DB978655 (DB923439)
DB978656 (DB923567)
DB978657 (DB924087)
DB978658 (DB923403)
DB978659 (DB923730)
DB978661 (DB924184)
DB978662 (DB924303)
DB978663 (DB923794)
DB978664 (DB923376)
DB978665 (DB924180)
DB978666 (DB923587)
DB978667 (DB924132)
DB978668 (DB923806)
DB978669 (DB923676)
DB978670 (DB924305)
DB978671 (DB923313)
DB978672 (DB923385)
DB978673 (DB923426)
DB978674 (DB924044)
DB978675 (DB923642)
DB978676 (DB924323)
DB978677 (DB924813)
DB978678 (DB924104)
DB978679 (DB923417)
DB978680 (DB923555)
DB978681 (DB924173)
DB978682 (DB923553)
DB978683 (DB923628)
DB978684 (DB923753)
DB978685 (DB923326)
DB978686 (DB924291)
DB978687 (DB924102)
DB978688 (DB923944)
DB978689 (DB923887)
DB978690 (DB923469)
DB978691 (DB923899)
DB978692 (DB923799)
DB978693 (DB923649)
DB978694 (DB923335)
DB978695 (DB923542)
DB978696 (DB923801)
DB978697 (DB923670)
DB978698 (DB923869)
DB978699 W(DB924393)
DB978700 (DB923416)
DB978701 (DB923384)
DB978702 (DB924888)
DB978703 W(DB923364)
DB978704 (DB924290)
DB978705 (DB924348)
DB978706 (DB924372)
DB978707 (DB923329)
DB978708 (DB924122)
DB978709 (DB923933)
DB978710 (DB924069)
DB978711 (DB923466)
DB978712 W(DB924388)
DB978713 (DB923574)
DB978716 W(DB923895)
DB978717 (DB923621)
DB978718 (DB924878)
DB978719 (DB923968)
DB978720 (DB923490)
DB978721 (DB924014)
DB978722 (DB923668)
DB978723 (DB924073)
DB978724 (DB924849)
DB978725 (DB923975)
DB978726 (DB923692)
DB978727 (DB924214)
DB978728 (DB923500)
DB978729 (DB923551)
DB978730 (DB923914)
DB978731 (DB924081)
DB978732 (DB924091)
DB978733 (DB923611)
DB978734 (DB924334)
DB978735 (DB923526)
DB978736 (DB923648)
DB978737 (DB923401)
DB978738 (DB923644)
DB978739 (DB923516)
DB978740 (DB923595)
DB978741 (DB924897)
DB978742 (DB924694)
DB978743 (DB923359)
DB978744 (DB924008)
DB978745 (DB923749)
DB978746 (DB923961)
DB978747 (DB924216)
DB978748 (DB923530)
DB978749= (DB924139)
DB978750 (DB924868)
DB978751 (DB923867)
DB978752 (DB923345)
DB978753 (DB924126)
DB978755 (DB924251)
DB978756 (DB924128)
DB978757 (DB923667)
DB978758 (DB924827)
DB978759 (DB923572)
DB978760= (DB923973)
DB978761 (DB923790)
DB978762 (DB923533)
DB978763 (DB923866)
DB978764 (DB923921)
DB978765 (DB923854)
DB978766 (DB924253)
DB978767 (DB923902)
DB978768 (DB923935)
DB978769 (DB923340)
DB978770 (DB924387)
DB978771 (DB923360)
DB978772 (DB924317)
DB978773 (DB924244)
DB978774 (DB923758)
DB978775 (DB924049)
DB978776 (DB924033)
DB978777 (DB923992)
DB978778 (DB923909)
DB978779 (DB924218)
DB978780 (DB924360)
DB978782 (DB924282)
DB978783 (DB924345)
DB978784 (DB924116)
DB978785 (DB923499)
DB978786 (DB923811)
DB978787 (DB923940)
DB978788 (DB924805)
DB978789 (DB924092)
DB978790 (DB923372)
DB978791 (DB923482)
DB978792 (DB923946)
DB978793 (DB924119)
DB978794 (DB923383)
DB978795 (DB924023)
DB978796 (DB923846)
DB978797 (DB923759)
DB978798 (DB923619)
DB978799 (DB924366)
DB978800 (DB923960)
DB978801 ( )
DB978802 (DB923309)
DB978804 (DB923414)
DB978805 W(DB924241)
DB978806 (DB924071)
DB978807 (DB923631)
DB978808 (DB923525)
DB978809 (DB924220)
DB978810 (DB924262)
DB978812 (DB924224)
DB978813 (DB924362)
DB978814 (DB923604)
DB978816 (DB923608)
DB978817 (DB924070)
DB978818 (DB924198)

DB978819	(DB923912)
DB978820	(DB924864)
DB978821	(DB924871)
DB978822	(DB924270)
DB978823	(DB923538)
DB978824	(DB923950)
DB978825	(DB924249)
DB978826	(DB923698)
DB978827	(DB923548)
DB978828	(DB924026)
DB978829	(DB923358)
DB978830	(DB924106)
DB978831	(DB923362)
DB978832	(DB924368)
DB978833	(DB923583)
DB978834	(DB923710)
DB978835	(DB924371)
DB978836	(DB923314)
DB978837	(DB924304)
DB978838	(DB923308)
DB978840	(DB924259)
DB978841	(DB923762)
DB978842	(DB923506)
DB978843	(DB923382)
DB978844	(DB924260)
DB978845	(DB924258)
DB978846	(DB924155)
DB978847	(DB923513)
DB978848	(DB923683)
DB978849	(DB924377)
DB978850	(DB923653)
DB978851	(DB923855)
DB978852	(DB924892)
DB978853	(DB923632)
DB978854	(DB924858)
DB978855	(DB923993)
DB978857	(DB923406)
DB978858	(DB924292)
DB978859	(DB923318)
DB978860	(DB923742)
DB978861	(DB924052)
DB978862	(DB924378)
DB978864	(DB924841)
DB978865	(DB924823)
DB978866	(DB923536)
DB978867	(DB924194)
DB978868	(DB923744)
DB978869	(DB924274)
DB978871	(DB924320)
DB978872	(DB923748)
DB978873	(DB924055)
DB978874	(DB924131)
DB978875	(DB923707)
DB978876	(DB923725)
DB978877	(DB924877)
DB978878	(DB924374)
DB978879	(DB923813)
DB978880	(DB924158)
DB978881	(DB923306)
DB978882	(DB924845)
DB978883	(DB924810)
DB978884	(DB924007)
DB978885	(DB924183)
DB978886	(DB924121)
DB978887	(DB924169)
DB978888	(DB924369)
DB978889	(DB923883)
DB978890	(DB923378)
DB978891	( )
DB978892	(DB924114)
DB978893	(DB923954)
DB978894	(DB923718)
DB978895	(DB924177)
DB978896	(DB923994)
DB978897	(DB924298)
DB978898	(DB924257)
DB978899	(DB924875)
DB978900	(DB924163)
DB978901	(DB923880)
DB978902	(DB924832)
DB978903	(DB924819)
DB978904	(DB923523)
DB978905	(DB923984)
DB978906	( )
DB978907	(DB923305)
DB978908	(DB924391)
DB978909	(DB923510)
DB978910	(DB924857)
DB978911	(DB923819)
DB978912	(DB923671)
DB978913	(DB923798)
DB978914	(DB924383)
DB978916	(DB924828)
DB978917	(DB924835)
DB978918	(DB923674)
DB978919	(DB924326)
DB978920	(DB924075)
DB978921	(DB923610)

DB978922	
DB978923	(W)
DB978925	
DB978927	(W)
DB978928	
DB978929	
DB978930	(W)
DB978931	
DB978932	
DB978933	(W)
DB978934	(W)
DB978935	(W)
DB978937	(W)
DB978938	
DB978940	
DB978941	(W)
DB978942	
DB978943	
DB978944	(W)
DB978945	
DB978946	
DB978947	(W)
DB978951	
DB978952	(W)
DB978953	(W)
DB978954	
DB978957	
DB978959	
DB978960	(W)
DB978961	
DB978962	
DB978963	
DB978964	(W)
DB978965	
DB978966	
DB978967	
DB978968	
DB978969	(W)
DB978970	
DB978971	(W)
DB978972	
DB978973	(W)
DB978974	(W)
DB978975	
DB978976	(W)
DB978977	
DB978978	
DB978979	
DB978980	
DB978981	
DB978982	
DB978983	(W)
DB978984	(W)
DB978986	
DB978987	
DB978989	(W)
DB978990	
DB978991	

Note: DB978922 - DB978991 supplied in kit form by BR (Swindon Works) to RFS Doncaster for completion and no former numbers are available.

Pictured at Ayr on 26th July 1990 is "Clam", ZCV, DB973352, a 21T Ballast Sleeper Wagon.
Paul W. Bartlett

Though subsequently withdrawn "Turbot", YCV, DB978953, a 34T Bogie Ballast Wagon, is seen at Tyne Yard on 24th September 1988.
Paul W. Bartlett

On 27th March 1994 40T Bogie Ballast Hopper Wagon, YGB, "Seacow", DB980175 is pictured at Eastleigh. Peter Ifold

YHA, "Whale", DB982360, a 50T Bogie Ballast Hopper Wagon, is pictured at Longport on 29th November 1992. Peter Ifold

YGH, "Seacow", DB982770, a 40T Bogie Ballast Hopper Wagon, is seen at Shettleston on 13th August 1991. Paul W. Bartlett

24T Ballast Hopper Wagon, ZFV, "Dogfish", DB983239 is pictured at Radyr on 20th August 1992. Paul W. Bartlett

Once a very common sight on BR the "Grampus" a 20T Ballast & Sleeper Wagon is becoming increasingly scarce. This recently withdrawn example, ZBV, DB985841 is pictured at Eastleigh on 27th March 1994.
Peter Ifold

A number of "Grampus" wagons received modifications and were reclassified as "Hake". An example of the latter, though since withdrawn, ZBA DB986147, a 20T Ballast & Sleeper Wagon, is photographed at Perth on 1st August 1989. Paul W. Bartlett

Number Series: DB979000 - DB979008

Description: 51T Welded Rail Bogie Wagon
Builder: BR (Shildon Works) Lot No.: 4015
Tare Weight: 30.1t Built: 1983
Design Code: YE001A G.L.W.: 62.0t
Fishkind: "PERCH" Tops Code: YEA

DB979000	DB979002	DB979004	DB979006	DB979008
DB979001	DB979003	DB979005	DB979007	

Number Series: DB979009 - DB979035

Description: 51T Welded Rail Bogie Wagon
Builder: BR (Doncaster Works) Lot No.: 4035
Tare Weight: 30.1t Built: 1984
Design Code: YE001A G.L.W.: 62.0t
Fishkind: "PERCH" Tops Code: YEA

DB979009	DB979015	DB979021	DB979026	DB979031
DB979010	DB979016	DB979022	DB979027	DB979032
DB979011	DB979017	DB979023	DB979028	DB979033
DB979012	DB979018	DB979024	DB979029	DB979034
DB979013	DB979019	DB979025	DB979030	DB979035
DB979014	DB979020			

Number Series: DB979036 - DB979083

Description: 51T Welded Rail Bogie Wagon
Builder: BR (Doncaster Works) Lot No.: 4047
Tare Weight: 30.1t Built: 1985
Design Code: YE007A G.L.W.: 62.0t
Fishkind: "PERCH" Tops Code: YEA

DB979036	DB979046	DB979056	DB979066	DB979075
DB979037	DB979047	DB979057	DB979067	DB979076
DB979038	DB979048	DB979058	DB979068	DB979077
DB979039	DB979049	DB979059	DB979069	DB979078
DB979040	DB979050	DB979060	DB979070	DB979079
DB979041	DB979051	DB979061	DB979071	DB979080
DB979042	DB979052	DB979062	DB979072	DB979081
DB979043	DB979053	DB979063	DB979073	DB979082
DB979044	DB979054	DB979064	DB979074	DB979083
DB979045	DB979055	DB979065		

Number Series: DB979084 - DB979131

Description: 51T Welded Rail Bogie Wagon
Builder: BR (Doncaster Works) Lot No.: 4055
Tare Weight: 30.9t Built: 1985
Design Code: YE007A G.L.W.: 62.0t
Fishkind: "PERCH" Tops Code: YEA

DB979084	DB979094	DB979104	DB979114	DB979123
DB979085	DB979095	DB979105	DB979115	DB979124
DB979086	DB979096	DB979106	DB979116	DB979125
DB979087	DB979097	DB979107	DB979117	DB979126
DB979088	DB979098	DB979108	DB979118	DB979127
DB979089	DB979099	DB979109	DB979119	DB979128
DB979090	DB979100	DB979110	DB979120	DB979129
DB979091	DB979101	DB979111	DB979121	DB979130
DB979092	DB979102	DB979112	DB979122	DB979131
DB979093	DB979103	DB979113		

Number Series: DB979400 - DB979409

Description: 51T Welded Rail Bogie Clamping Wagon
Builder: BR (Doncaster Works) Lot No.: 4045
Tare Weight: 31.4t Built: 1985
Design Code: YE007A G.L.W.: 63.0t
Fishkind: "PERCH" Tops Code: YEA

DB979400	DB979402	DB979404	DB979406	DB979408
DB979401	DB979403	DB979405	DB979407	DB979409

Number Series: DB979410 - DB979415

Description: 51T Welded Rail Bogie Clamping Wagon
Builder: BR (Doncaster Works) Lot No.: 4053
Tare Weight: 31.4t Built: 1985
Design Code: YE010A G.L.W.: 63.0t
Fishkind: "PERCH" Tops Code: YEA

DB979410	DB979412	DB979413	DB979414	DB979415
DB979411				

Number Series: DB979500 - DB979501

Description: 18T Welded Rail Bogie Chute Wagon
Builder: BR (Shildon Works) Lot No.: 4016
Tare Weight: 36.8t Built: 1982
Design Code: YE002A G.L.W.: 37.0t
Fishkind: "PORPOISE" Tops Code: YEA

DB979500 DB979501

Number Series: DB979502 - DB979503

Description: 18T Welded Rail Bogie Chute Wagon
Builder: BR (Shildon Works) Lot No.: 4036
Tare Weight: 36.8t Built: 1983
Design Code: YE005A G.L.W.: 37.0t
Fishkind: "PORPOISE" Tops Code: YEA

DB979502 DB979503

Number Series: DB979504 - DB979509

Description: 18T Welded Rail Bogie Chute Wagon
Builder: BR (Crewe Works) Lot No.: 4046
Tare Weight: 36.8t Built: 1985
Design Code: YE006A G.L.W.: 37.0t
Fishkind: "PORPOISE" Tops Code: YEA

DB979504 DB979506 DB979507 DB979508 DB979509
DB979505

Number Series: DB979510 - DB979515

Description: 18T Welded Rail Bogie Chute Wagon
Builder: BR (Crewe Works) Lot No.: 4054
Tare Weight: 36.8t Built: 1985
Design Code: YE006A G.L.W.: 37.0t
Fishkind: "PORPOISE" Tops Code: YEA

DB979510 DB979512 DB979513 DB979514 DB979515
DB979511

Number Series: DB979600 - DB979603

Description: Welded Rail Bogie Stabling Wagon
Builder: BR (Shildon Works) Lot No.: 4037
Tare Weight: 30.6t Built: 1982-83
Design Code: YE004A G.L.W.: 66.0t
Fishkind: "PERCH" Tops Code: YEA

DB979600 DB979601 DB979602 DB979603

Number Series: DB979604 - DB979609

Description: Welded Rail Bogie Stabling Wagon
Builder: BR (Doncaster Works) Lot No.: 4044
Tare Weight: 30.6t Built: 1985
Design Code: YE004A G.L.W.: 66.0t
Fishkind: "PERCH" Tops Code: YEA

DB979604 DB979606 DB979607 DB979608 DB979609
DB979605

Number Series: DB979610 - DB979615

Description: Welded Rail Bogie Stabling Wagon
Builder: BR (Doncaster Works) Lot No.: 4052
Tare Weight: 30.6t Built: 1985-86
Design Code: YE004A G.L.W.: 66.0t
Fishkind: "PERCH" Tops Code: YEA

DB979610	DB979612	DB979613	DB979614	DB979615
DB979611				

Number Series: DB980000 - DB980244

Description: 40T Bogie Ballast Hopper Wagon
Builder: BREL (Ashford/Shildon Works) Lot No.: 3966
Tare Weight: 21.25t * 21.3t Built: 1981-82
Design Code: YE004A YE004M * YE004R + G.L.W.: 62.0t
Fishkind: "SEACOW" "STINGRAY" * Tops Code: YGB

DB980000	DB980047	DB980094	DB980141	DB980188
DB980001	DB980048	DB980095	DB980142	DB980189
DB980002	DB980049	DB980096*	DB980143*	DB980190
DB980003	DB980050	DB980097	DB980144	DB980191
DB980004	DB980051	DB980098	DB980145	DB980192
DB980005	DB980052	DB980099	DB980146	DB980193
DB980006	DB980053+	DB980100+	DB980147	DB980194
DB980007	DB980054+	DB980101	DB980148*	DB980195
DB980008	DB980055*	DB980102+	DB980149	DB980196
DB980009	DB980056+	DB980103	DB980150	DB980197
DB980010	DB980057+	DB980104+	DB980151	DB980198
DB980011	DB980058	DB980105+	DB980152	DB980199
DB980012	DB980059	DB980106	DB980153	DB980200
DB980013	DB980060	DB980107	DB980154*	DB980201
DB980014	DB980061	DB980108	DB980155	DB980202
DB980015	DB980062+	DB980109	DB980156	DB980203
DB980016	DB980063	DB980110	DB980157	DB980204
DB980017	DB980064	DB980111	DB980158	DB980205
DB980018	DB980065	DB980112	DB980159	DB980206
DB980019	DB980066	DB980113	DB980160	DB980207
DB980020	DB980067	DB980114+	DB980161	DB980208
DB980021	DB980068	DB980115+	DB980162	DB980209
DB980022	DB980069	DB980116	DB980163+	DB980210+
DB980023	DB980070	DB980117	DB980164	DB980211
DB980024	DB980071	DB980118+	DB980165	DB980212+
DB980025	DB980072	DB980119	DB980166	DB980213
DB980026	DB980073+	DB980120+	DB980167	DB980214
DB980027	DB980074	DB980121	DB980168	DB980215
DB980028	DB980075	DB980122	DB980169	DB980216
DB980029	DB980076	DB980123	DB980170	DB980217
DB980030	DB980077	DB980124	DB980171+	DB980218
DB980031	DB980078+	DB980125+	DB980172*	DB980219
DB980032	DB980079	DB980126+	DB980173	DB980220
DB980033	DB980080	DB980127+	DB980174	DB980221
DB980034	DB980081	DB980128+	DB980175	DB980222
DB980035	DB980082	DB980129	DB980176+	DB980223
DB980036	DB980083	DB980130	DB980177	DB980224
DB980037	DB980084	DB980131*	DB980178	DB980225
DB980038	DB980085	DB980132	DB980179+	DB980226
DB980039	DB980086	DB980133	DB980180	DB980227
DB980040	DB980087	DB980134*	DB980181+	DB980228
DB980041	DB980088	DB980135	DB980182	DB980229
DB980042	DB980089	DB980136	DB980183	DB980230
DB980043	DB980090	DB980137*	DB980184	DB980231
DB980044	DB980091	DB980138*	DB980185	DB980232
DB980045	DB980092	DB980139	DB980186+	DB980233
DB980046	DB980093	DB980140*	DB980187+	DB980234

DB980235	DB980237	DB980239	DB980241	DB980243
DB980236	DB980238	DB980240	DB980242	DB980244

Number Series: DB980245 - DB980250

Description: 40T Bogie Ballast Hopper Wagon
Builder: BR (Shildon Works) — Lot No.: 4010
Tare Weight: 21.3t — Built: 1981-82
Design Code: YG500H — G.L.W.: 62.0t
Fishkind: "SEACOW" — Tops Code: YGB

DB980245	DB980247	DB980248	DB980249	DB980250
DB980246				

Number Series: DB981000 - DB981001

Description: 52T Bogie Ballast/Sleeper Carrier
Builder: BR (Shildon Works) — Lot No.: 4006
Tare Weight: 24.2t — Built: 1980
Design Code: YC501A — G.L.W.: 80.0t
Fishkind: "HALIBUT" — Tops Code: YCA

DB981000 — DB981001

Number Series: DB982054 - DB982120

Description: 12T Ballast Wagon — Lot No.: 2012
Builder: BR (Wolverton Works) — Built: 1949
Diagram No.: 1/565 — G.L.W.: 19.0t
Tare Weight: 7.5t — Tops Code: ZCA
Design Code: ZC505A — Fishkind: "SOLE"

DB982054 DB982120

Number Series: DB982197

Description: 12T Ballast Wagon — Lot No.: 2264
Builder: BR (Wolverton Works) — Built: 1949
Diagram No.: 1/565 — G.L.W.: 19.0t
Tare Weight: 7.5t — Tops Code: ZCA
Design Code: ZC505A — Fishkind: "SOLE"

DB982197

Number Series: DB982350 - DB982439

Description: 50T Bogie Ballast Hopper Wagon
Builder: BR (Shildon Works)
Diagram No.: 1/589
Tare Weight: 23.8t
Design Code: YH500B YH500C +

Lot No.: 3591
Built: 1966-67
G.L.W.: 36.0t
Tops Code: YHA
Fishkind: "WHALE"

DB982350
DB982351
DB982352
DB982353
DB982354
DB982355
DB982356
DB982357
DB982358
DB982360+
DB982361
DB982362
DB982363
DB982364
DB982365
DB982366
DB982367
DB982368
DB982369
DB982370
DB982371
DB982372
DB982373
DB982374
DB982375
DB982376
DB982377
DB982378
DB982379
DB982380
DB982381
DB982382+
DB982383
DB982384+
DB982385
DB982386
DB982387
DB982388
DB982389
DB982390
DB982391
DB982392
DB982393
DB982395
DB982396
DB982397
DB982398
DB982399
DB982400
DB982401
DB982402
DB982403
DB982404
DB982405
DB982406
DB982407
DB982408
DB982409 (W)
DB982410
DB982411
DB982412
DB982413
DB982414
DB982415
DB982416
DB982417
DB982418
DB982419+
DB982420+
DB982421
DB982422+
DB982423
DB982424
DB982425
DB982427
DB982428
DB982429
DB982430
DB982431+
DB982432
DB982433
DB982434
DB982435
DB982436
DB982437
DB982438
DB982439

Number Series: DB982440 - DB982539

Description: 40T Bogie Ballast Hopper Wagon
Builder: BR (Shildon Works)
Diagram No.: 1/590
Tare Weight: 21.25t + 21.3t
Design Code: YG500B YG500G = YG500L %
YG500Q + YG500S ! YG500T *
YG500U #
Fishkind: "SEALION" "STINGRAY" *

Lot No.: 3723
Built: 1971
G.L.W.: 62.7t = 63.0t
Tops Code: YGH

DB982440
DB982441
DB982442+
DB982443*
DB982444=
DB982445=
DB982446
DB982447%
DB982448=
DB982449=
DB982450=
DB982451!
DB982452%
DB982453+
DB982454+
DB982455+
DB982456+
DB982457+
DB982458=
DB982459=
DB982460+
DB982461=
DB982462=
DB982463=
DB982464+
DB982465%
DB982466=
DB982467=
DB982468=
DB982469=
DB982470*
DB982471=
DB982472
DB982473=
DB982474=
DB982475=
DB982476*
DB982477*
DB982478=
DB982479%
DB982480=
DB982481+
DB982482+
DB982483=
DB982484=
DB982485=
DB982486+
DB982487+
DB982488+
DB982489%
DB982490!
DB982491+
DB982492!
DB982493=
DB982494
DB982495*
DB982496+
DB982497
DB982498+
DB982499
DB982500!
DB982501
DB982502=
DB982503+
DB982504*
DB982505
DB982506
DB982507
DB982508
DB982509
DB982510+
DB982511
DB982512+
DB982513
DB982514+
DB982515
DB982516
DB982517+
DB982518+
DB982519
DB982520
DB982521+
DB982522
DB982523%
DB982524
DB982525+
DB982526
DB982527
DB982528+
DB982529+
DB982530
DB982531!
DB982532
DB982533+
DB982534
DB982535+
DB982536
DB982537+
DB982538
DB982539!

Number Series: DB982540 - DB982564

Description: 40T Bogie Ballast Hopper Wagon
Built: BR (Shildon Works) — Lot No.: 3724
Diagram No.: 1/591 — Built: 1971
Tare Weight: 21.25t + 21.3t — G.L.W.: 62.0t
Design Code: YG500A YG500K + YG500U # YG500V * — Tops Code: YGB
Fishkind: "SEACOW"

DB982540+	DB982545	DB982550	DB982555+	DB982560+
DB982541	DB982546+	DB982551	DB982556+	DB982561+
DB982542	DB982547	DB982552	DB982557	DB982562
DB982543	DB982548+	DB982553	DB982558+	DB982563#
DB982544	DB982549*	DB982554	DB982559	DB982564

Number Series: DB982565 - DB982657

Description: 40T Bogie Ballast Hopper Wagon — Lot No.: 3777
Builder: BR (Shildon Works) — Built: 1971
Diagram No.: 1/591 — G.L.W.: 62.0t
Tare Weight: 21.3t — Tops Code: YGB
Design Code: YG500A — Fishkind: "SEACOW"

DB982565	DB982566	DB982567

Number Series: DB982568 - DB982927

Description: 40T Bogie Ballast Hopper Wagon
Builder: BR (Shildon Works) — Lot No.: 3802
Diagram No.: 1/590 — Built: 1972-74
Tare Weight: 21.3t — G.L.W.: 62.0t
Design Code: YG500A ^ YG500B YG500G = YG500L - YG500S ! YG500T * YG500Q + — Tops Code: YGH
Fishkind: "SEALION" "SEACOW" -+ "STINGRAY" *

DB982568!	DB982588*	DB982608-	DB982628=	DB982650=
DB982569-	DB982589+	DB982609	DB982629-	DB982651=
DB982570+	DB982590=	DB982610	DB982630*	DB982652=
DB982571=	DB982591	DB982611	DB982631+	DB982654+
DB982572=	DB982592+	DB982612+	DB982632	DB982655=
DB982573-	DB982593=	DB982613	DB982633!	DB982656!
DB982574=	DB982594-	DB982614*	DB982634	DB982657+
DB982575-	DB982595=	DB982615-	DB982635	DB982658=
DB982576+	DB982596+	DB982616-	DB982637	DB982659*
DB982577-	DB982597=	DB982617	DB982638	DB982660
DB982578=	DB982598-	DB982618	DB982639	DB982661+
DB982579=	DB982599	DB982619-	DB982640	DB982662-
DB982580*	DB982600+	DB982620+	DB982641	DB982663=
DB982581=	DB982601*	DB982621	DB982642	DB982664-
DB982582=	DB982602!	DB982622+	DB982643	DB982665=
DB982583=	DB982603	DB982623	DB982644	DB982666=
DB982584	DB982604	DB982624+	DB982645!	DB982667+
DB982585-	DB982605!	DB982625	DB982647#	DB982668=
DB982586-	DB982606*	DB982626	DB982648+	DB982669+
DB982587=	DB982607+	DB982627=	DB982649=	DB982670+

DB982671+
DB982672-
DB982673=
DB982674=
DB982675+
DB982676+
DB982677-
DB982678=
DB982679=
DB982680=
DB982681+
DB982682=
DB982683+
DB982684=
DB982685-
DB982686-
DB982687=
DB982688=
DB982689+
DB982690+
DB982691=
DB982692+
DB982693=
DB982694=
DB982695=
DB982696=
DB982697-
DB982698=
DB982699-
DB982700=
DB982701=
DB982702+
DB982703=
DB982704=
DB982705+
DB982706=
DB982707=
DB982708=
DB982709
DB982710+
DB982711
DB982712+
DB982713*
DB982714-
DB982715+
DB982716!
DB982717
DB982718
DB982719
DB982720
DB982721
DB982722+
DB982723-
DB982724
DB982725
DB982726!
DB982727
DB982728-
DB982729
DB982730
DB982732
DB982733
DB982734
DB982735
DB982736
DB982737+
DB982738
DB982739
DB982740
DB982741+
DB982742+
DB982743^
DB982744
DB982745^
DB982746+
DB982747+
DB982748+
DB982749+
DB982750+
DB982751
DB982752+
DB982753
DB982754
DB982755+
DB982756+
DB982757+
DB982758
DB982759*
DB982760-
DB982761+
DB982762!
DB982763
DB982765
DB982766
DB982767*
DB982768+
DB982769
DB982770+
DB982771
DB982773
DB982774
DB982775+
DB982776
DB982777
DB982778+
DB982779
DB982780
DB982781-
DB982782
DB982783
DB982784-
DB982785-
DB982786
DB982787-
DB982788-
DB982789
DB982790
DB982791-
DB982792-
DB982793
DB982794
DB982795-
DB982796-
DB982797+
DB982798
DB982799!
DB982800
DB982801
DB982802*
DB982803
DB982804-
DB982805
DB982806
DB982807
DB982808-
DB982809+
DB982810
DB982811+
DB982812
DB982813
DB982814
DB982815+
DB982816
DB982817+
DB982818+
DB982819+
DB982820
DB982821!
DB982822!
DB982823
DB982824
DB982825*
DB982826
DB982827
DB982828
DB982829+
DB982830!
DB982831
DB982832
DB982833
DB982834=
DB982835+
DB982836-
DB982837
DB982838
DB982839
DB982840+
DB982841
DB982842
DB982843
DB982844+
DB982845
DB982846!
DB982847
DB982848
DB982849+
DB982850
DB982851
DB982852
DB982853
DB982854-
DB982855
DB982856+
DB982857
DB982858
DB982859+
DB982860
DB982861
DB982862+
DB982863
DB982864!
DB982865+
DB982866+
DB982867+
DB982868
DB982869+
DB982870*
DB982871+
DB982872+
DB982873=
DB982874-
DB982875
DB982876=
DB982877=
DB982878=
DB982879-
DB982880=
DB982881
DB982882-
DB982883=
DB982884-
DB982885=
DB982886-
DB982887+
DB982888=
DB982889*
DB982890+
DB982891-
DB982892=
DB982893
DB982894+
DB982895
DB982896=
DB982897!
DB982898
DB982899+
DB982900
DB982901*
DB982902
DB982903
DB982904-
DB982905
DB982906
DB982907
DB982908+
DB982909
DB982910-
DB982911
DB982912
DB982913+
DB982914*
DB982915+
DB982916
DB982917+
DB982918
DB982919
DB982920+
DB982921
DB982922-
DB982923*
DB982924
DB982925=
DB982926-
DB982927

Number Series: DB983000 - DB983309

Description: 24T Ballast Hopper Wagon
Builder: Charles Roberts Ltd
Diagram No.: 1/587
Tare Weight: 12.0t
Design Code: ZF501A ZF501B + ZF501C #
ZF501D = ZF501F *
Fishkind: "DOGFISH"

Lot No.: 2939
Built: 1957
G.L.W.: 36.5t
Tops Code: ZFW *= ZFV

DB983000
DB983001+
DB983002
DB983003+
DB983004+
DB983005
DB983006
DB983007+
DB983009+
DB983010+
DB983014
DB983016+
DB983017*
DB983018+
DB983019+
DB983021+
DB983022
DB983023+
DB983024+
DB983025+
DB983026+
DB983027+
DB983029
DB983030+
DB983031+
DB983032
DB983033+
DB983034+
DB983035+
DB983037
DB983039+
DB983040=
DB983041+
DB983042+
DB983043+
DB983044+
DB983045+
DB983046+
DB983049+
DB983050+(W)
DB983051+
DB983053+
DB983056+
DB983057+
DB983058+
DB983059
DB983060+
DB983061+
DB983063+
DB983064
DB983065+
DB983066+
DB983067+
DB983068
DB983070+
DB983071+
DB983072+
DB983073
DB983075
DB983076+
DB983077+
DB983078
DB983079*
DB983080+
DB983081+
DB983082*
DB983083+
DB983084
DB983085
DB983086+
DB983087=
DB983088+
DB983091+
DB983093+
DB983094+
DB983095
DB983096+
DB983097+
DB983098+
DB983099+
DB983100+
DB983101+
DB983102
DB983103
DB983104*
DB983105+
DB983107+
DB983108+
DB983109+
DB983111+
DB983112
DB983113
DB983114
DB983115
DB983116+
DB983118+
DB983121
DB983122
DB983123+
DB983124+
DB983125+
DB983127+
DB983128+
DB983129+
DB983132+
DB983133+
DB983134+
DB983135
DB983136+
DB983137
DB983138
DB983139
DB983140
DB983141+
DB983143
DB983144+
DB983146+(W)
DB983147+
DB983148+
DB983149+
DB983151+
DB983153+
DB983154
DB983155+
DB983157+
DB983159+
DB983160+
DB983161+
DB983162
DB983163+
DB983167+
DB983168+
DB983169+
DB983170+
DB983172+
DB983174+
DB983175+
DB983177+
DB983179
DB983181+
DB983182+
DB983183
DB983184+
DB983186+
DB983187+
DB983188+
DB983192+
DB983193+
DB983194+
DB983195+
DB983196+
DB983197+
DB983198+
DB983201+
DB983202+
DB983203+
DB983208+
DB983209+
DB983210+
DB983211+
DB983213+
DB983214+
DB983215+
DB983216+
DB983217+
DB983219+
DB983222+
DB983223+
DB983224
DB983225+
DB983226+
DB983227+
DB983228+
DB983230+
DB983231+
DB983232+
DB983233+
DB983235+
DB983239+
DB983240+
DB983243+
DB983244+
DB983245+
DB983246+
DB983247+
DB983249+(W)
DB983250+
DB983251+
DB983253+
DB983257+
DB983259#
DB983260+
DB983261#
DB983263#
DB983264+
DB983265#
DB983266#
DB983267#
DB983269#
DB983270+(W)
DB983271#
DB983274#
DB983275+
DB983276#
DB983278#
DB983280#
DB983281#
DB983282#
DB983285#
DB983292+
DB983293#
DB983295#(W)
DB983299#
DB983301+
DB983302+
DB983303+
DB983305+
DB983307#
DB983309#

Number Series: DB983376 - DB983576

Description: 19T Ballast Hopper Wagon
Builder: Metropolitan Cammell Ltd — Lot No.: 3039
Diagram No.: 1/586 — Built: 1961
Tare Weight: 9.8t — G.L.W.: 9.8t + 30.0t
Design Code: ZE500A ZE500B # ZE500C * ZS152A + — Tops Code: ZEV ZSV +
Fishkind: "CATFISH"

DB983376#
DB983377#
DB983378#
DB983379#
DB983380#
DB983381
DB983383#
DB983385#
DB983388#
DB983389#
DB983390#
DB983391
DB983392#
DB983395#
DB983396#
DB983397#
DB983398
DB983399
DB983400
DB983402#
DB983403#
DB983404#
DB983405+
DB983406#
DB983407#
DB983409
DB983411#
DB983412#
DB983413#
DB983414#(W)
DB983415#
DB983416#
DB983417#
DB983418#
DB983419#
DB983420#
DB983421#
DB983422
DB983423#
DB983425
DB983427#
DB983428#
DB983431#
DB983432#
DB983434#
DB983435#
DB983436#
DB983437#
DB983438#
DB983440#
DB983444#
DB983446#
DB983447#
DB983448#
DB983449#
DB983450
DB983452#
DB983453#
DB983454#
DB983455#
DB983457
DB983458
DB983459#
DB983463#
DB983464#
DB983466#
DB983468
DB983469#
DB983470#
DB983471#
DB983473
DB983476#
DB983481
DB983482
DB983483
DB983485
DB983486#
DB983489#
DB983491#
DB983492#
DB983493#
DB983495*
DB983496#
DB983497#
DB983498#
DB983500#
DB983503#(W)
DB983505#
DB983508
DB983509#
DB983510
DB983511#
DB983512#
DB983514#
DB983516#
DB983517
DB983518#
DB983519#
DB983520
DB983521#
DB983522#
DB983526#
DB983527#
DB983528
DB983532 (W)
DB983533#
DB983534
DB983535 (W)
DB983536#
DB983537#
DB983538#
DB983541#
DB983542#
DB983543
DB983546#
DB983547#
DB983549
DB983550#
DB983551#
DB983553#
DB983554
DB983556#
DB983557
DB983558
DB983559#
DB983560#
DB983562#
DB983563#
DB983564#
DB983565#(W)
DB983568#
DB983570
DB983571#
DB983572#
DB983575#
DB983576#

Number Series: DB983577 - DB983626

Description: 24T Ballast Hopper Wagon
Builder: BR (Shildon Works) — Lot No.: 3329
Diagram No.: 1/587 — Built: 1961
Tare Weight: 11.5t — G.L.W.: 36.5t
Design Code: YE007A — Tops Code: ZFV
Fishkind: "DOGFISH"

DB983577
DB983578
DB983579
DB983580
DB983581
DB983582
DB983583
DB983584
DB983585
DB983586
DB983587
DB983588
DB983589
DB983590
DB983591
DB983593
DB983594
DB983595
DB983596
DB983597
DB983598
DB983599
DB983601
DB983602
DB983603
DB983604
DB983605
DB983607
DB983608
DB983609
DB983610
DB983611
DB983612
DB983613
DB983615
DB983616
DB983617
DB983618
DB983619
DB983620
DB983621
DB983622
DB983623
DB983624
DB983625
DB983626

Number Series: DB983627 - DB983895

Description: 19T Ballast Hopper Wagon
Builder: Metropolitan Cammell Ltd — Lot No.: 3331
Diagram No.: 1/586 — Built: 1960-61
Tare Weight: 9.8t — G.L.W.: 30.0t
Design Code: ZE500A ZE500B # ZE500C + ZS152A * — Tops Code: ZEV ZSV *
Fishkind: "CATFISH"

DB983627
DB983628#
DB983629#
DB983632
DB983633
DB983636#
DB983637#
DB983638
DB983639#
DB983640#
DB983641#
DB982642
DB983643#
DB983644
DB983645#
DB983646#
DB983647
DB983648
DB983650#
DB983651#
DB983652#
DB983654#
DB983655#
DB983656#
DB983657#
DB983658#
DB983659#(W)
DB983660#
DB983661#
DB983664#
DB983665
DB983666
DB983667#
DB983668#
DB983669
DB983670#
DB983671
DB983672+
DB983673#
DB983674#
DB983675
DB983677#
DB983678#
DB983679
DB983680#
DB983681#
DB983682#
DB983683#
DB983684
DB983685#
DB983688
DB983689#
DB983690#
DB983691#
DB983692#
DB983694#
DB983695#
DB983697#
DB983698#
DB983700#
DB983702#
DB983703
DB983704#
DB983703#
DB983706
DB983707#
DB983708#
DB983709#
DB983710
DB983711#
DB983712#
DB983713
DB983714
DB983715#
DB983716#
DB983717
DB983718#
DB983720#
DB983721#
DB983722#
DB983724#
DB983725#
DB983726
DB983727 (W)
DB983728#
DB983729#
DB983730#
DB983732
DB983733#
DB983734#
DB983735#
DB983736#
DB983737#
DB983738#
DB983740#
DB983741
DB983743#
DB983745#
DB983747#
DB983748#
DB983749#
DB983750#
DB983751#
DB983752#
DB983753#
DB983754#
DB983755#
DB983756#
DB983758
DB983759#
DB983761#
DB983762
DB983766#
DB983768#
DB983769
DB983770
DB983771#
DB983772
DB983773#
DB983774#
DB983775#(W)
DB983776
DB983777
DB983780
DB983781
DB983782#
DB983783#
DB983784#
DB983785#
DB983787#
DB983788#
DB983789#
DB983791#
DB983792#
DB983793
DB983794#
DB983795#
DB982797#
DB983799#
DB983800#
DB983802*
DB983804#
DB983805
DB983806#
DB983809#
DB983810#
DB983811#
DB983812#
DB983813
DB983814
DB983815#
DB983816#
DB983817#
DB983819#
DB983820#
DB983821#
DB983822#
DB983823#
DB983824#
DB983827
DB983828#
DB983831#
DB983832#
DB983833#
DB983834#
DB983835#
DB983836#
DB983837#
DB983839#
DB983841#
DB983842#
DB983843
DB983844
DB983845#
DB983846#
DB983847#
DB983848#
DB983849#
DB983850#
DB983851#
DB983852#
DB983853#
DB983854#
DB983856
DB983857#
DB983858
DB983859#
DB983860#
DB983861
DB983862#
DB983863#
DB983864#
DB983865
DB983866
DB983867#
DB983868#
DB983869#
DB983870#
DB983871#
DB983872
DB983873#
DB983874
DB983875#
DB983876
DB983877
DB983878#
DB983879*
DB983880#
DB983881#
DB983882#
DB983883#
DB983884#
DB983885#
DB983886#
DB983887#
DB983888#
DB983889#
DB983890#
DB983891#
DB983892#
DB983893#
DB983894#
DB983895

Number Series: DB983897 - DB983920

Description: 24T Ballast Hopper Wagon
Builder: BR (Shildon Works) Lot No.: 3340
Diagram No.: 1/587 Built: 1961
Tare Weight: 11.5t 11.8t # G.L.W.: 36.5t
Design Code: ZF001B ZF001C # Tops Code: ZFV
Fishkind: "DOGFISH"

DB983897	DB983902	DB983910#	DB983914	DB983917
DB983899#	DB983906	DB983911#	DB983915	DB983918
DB983900	DB983908#	DB983912#	DB983916	DB983920
DB983901	DB983909	DB983913#		

Number Series: DB984032 - DB984043

Description: 20T Ballast & Sleeper Wagon
Builder: Gloucester R C & W Co Ltd Lot No.: 2942
Diagram No.: 1/572 Built: 1956
Tare Weight: 10.0t G.L.W.: 30.5t
Design Code: ZB501A Tops Code: ZBO
Fishkind: "GRAMPUS"

DB984032	DB984043

Number Series: DB984061 - DB984210

Description: 20T Ballast & Sleeper Wagon
Builder: Cambrian Wagon Works Lot No.: 3038
Diagram No.: 1/572 Built: 1957-58
Tare Weight: 10.0t 10.5t #* G.L.W.: 30.5t 31.0t #
Design Code: ZB501A ZB501K = ZB501M + ZB501T # ZB501U * Tops Code: ZBA * ZBO ZBV += ZBW #
Fishkind: "GRAMPUS" "RUDD" *

DB984061+(W)	DB984075*	DB984098=(W)	DB984159+(W)	DB984210=(W)
DB984071#(W)	DB984082=(W)	DB984113	DB984194=	

Number Series: DB984284 - DB984302

Description: 20T Ballast & Sleeper Wagon
Builder: Butterley Engineering Co Ltd Lot No.: 3048
Diagram No.: 1/572 Built: 1957
Tare Weight: 10.0t G.L.W.: 30.5t
Design Code: ZB501K + ZB501M Tops Code: ZBO ZBV +
Fishkind: "GRAMPUS"

DB984284+	DB984286+(W)	DB984290+(W)	DB984295+	DB984299+
DB984285+	DB984287+(W)	DB984292+	DB984296+(W)	DB984302

Number Series: DB984313 - DB984537

Description: 20T Ballast & Sleeper Wagon
Builder: Butterley Engineering Co Ltd
Lot No.: 3049
Diagram No.: 1/572
Built: 1957-58
Tare Weight: 10.0t 10.5t -
G.L.W.: 30.5t 31.0t *-
Design Code: ZB501A + ZB501K = ZB501M ZB501Q # ZB501T - ZC013B *
Tops Code: ZBO ZCV * ZBV +-=#
Fishkind: "GRAMPUS" "EGRET" *

DB984313	DB984331 (W)	DB984349	DB984376	DB984401 (W)
DB984316=	DB984333	DB984351	DB984384=	DB984403-
DB984318=	DB984334	DB984353=(W)	DB984385	DB984404 (W)
DB984320	DB984336=	DB984358	DB984390 (W)	DB984406=
DB984321=	DB984341=(W)	DB984361=	DB984391=	DB984407=(W)
DB984323=(W)	DB984342#	DB984364 (W)	DB984392=	DB984408=
DB984325 (W)	DB984344*	DB984365	DB984396	DB984417#
DB984326=	DB984346	DB984372 (W)	DB984398	DB984491=
DB984327=	DB984347=(W)	DB984373*	DB984399	DB984537+
DB984329=				

Number Series: DB984550 - DB984645

Description: 20T Ballast & Sleeper Wagon
Builder: Derbyshire C & W Co Ltd
Lot No.: 3050
Diagram No.: 1/572
Built: 1957-58
Tare Weight: 10.0t 10.5t -
G.L.W.: 30.5t 31.0t -
Design Code: ZB501A + ZB501K = ZB501Q ZB501U * ZX112B -
Tops Code: ZBA * ZBV ZXO -
Fishkind: "GRAMPUS" "RUDD" *

DB984550 (W)	DB984595+	DB984613+	DB984629*	DB984645+
DB984556=(W)	DB984612-			

Number Series: DB984696 - DB984966

Description: 20T Ballast & Sleeper Wagon
Builder: Gloucester R C & W Co Ltd
Lot No.: 3052
Diagram No.: 1/572
Built: 1957
Tare Weight: 9.0t % 9.1t + 9.75t * 10.5t
G.L.W.: 29.5t % 30.5t
Design Code: ZB501A + ZB501M ZB501Q # ZB501U * ZX501P %
Tops Code: ZBA * ZBO + ZBQ # ZBV ZXQ %
Fishkind: "GRAMPUS" "RUDD" *

DB984696#	DB984745	DB984837*	DB984874	DB984945+
DB984715+	DB984785#	DB984849*	DB984896*	DB984966#
DB984724	DB984827%	DB984870 (W)		

Number Series: DB985014 - DB985341

Description: 20T Ballast & Sleeper Wagon
Builder: Butterley Engineering Co Ltd | Lot No.: 2362
Diagram No.: 1/572 | Built: 1952-55
Tare Weight: 9.1t + 9.75t # 10.5t | G.L.W.: 30.5t 31.0t *!
Design Code: ZB501A + ZB501B ! ZB501K ZB501M % ZB501U # ZC013B * | Tops Code: ZBO + ZBV ZBA # ZCV *
Fishkind: "GRAMPUS" "EGRET" * "RUDD" #

DB985014+	DB985056%	DB985079%(W)	DB985117%	DB985278
DB985018%	DB985057%	DB985091%(W)	DB985119%	DB985284%
DB985023 (W)	DB985059 (W)	DB985092%	DB985121%	DB985286%
DB985039%	DB985060 (W)	DB985094 (W)	DB985128 (W)	DB985287%(W)
DB985042	DB985062%(W)	DB985099%	DB985156%	DB985288 (W)
DB985043%(W)	DB985064	DB985103%(W)	DB985173*	DB985300#
DB985045%(W)	DB985065%(W)	DB985104	DB985209!	DB985301%
DB985046	DB985066	DB985106	DB985269 (W)	DB985303 (W)
DB985047%(W)	DB985067	DB985107%(W)	DB985270%(W)	DB985307 (W)
DB985049%	DB985070%	DB985109%	DB985272 (W)	DB985336#
DB985050 (W)	DB985072 (W)	DB985113%	DB985273%(W)	DB985339%(W)
DB985052%(W)	DB985074	DB985114 (W)	DB985275%	DB985341
DB985053 (W)	DB985077 (W)	DB985115%	DB985276%(W)	

Number Series: DB985411 - DB985641

Description: 20T Ballast & Sleeper Wagon
Builder: BR (Shildon Works) | Lot No.: 2482
Diagram No.: 1/572 | Built: 1954-55
Tare Weight: 9.1t + 10.5t | G.L.W.: 30.5t
Design Code: ZB501A + ZB501K = ZB501M ZB501U * | Tops Code: ZBA * ZBO + ZBV
Fishkind: "GRAMPUS" "RUDD" *

DB985411 (W)	DB985565 (W)	DB985578	DB985610=	DB985628
DB985496+	DB985566 (W)	DB985579=(W)	DB985611	DB985629
DB985498 (W)	DB985567	DB985580=	DB985613 (W)	DB985631=(W)
DB985507+(W)	DB985568	DB985582=(W)	DB985617=	DB985632=(W)
DB985517	DB985571 (W)	DB985591=(W)	DB985621	DB985633 (W)
DB985531	DB985572	DB985603	DB985622	DB985635 (W)
DB985544*	DB985574=(W)	DB985604	DB985623	DB985636
DB985554	DB985575+	DB985607=(W)	DB985624	DB985639 (W)
DB985561*	DB985576 (W)	DB985608=	DB985626	DB985641 (W)
DB985563	DB985577 (W)	DB985609 (W)	DB985627	

Number Series: DB985683 - DB985882

Description: 20T Ballast & Sleeper Wagon
Builder: BR (Shildon Works) | Lot No.: 2483
Diagram No: 1/572 | Built: 1954-55
Tare Weight: 9.1t + 9.75t # 10.5t | G.L.W.: 30.5t 31.0t *
Design Code: ZB501A + ZB501B ! ZB501K = ZB501Q # ZB501M ZB501U ! ZB501T * | Tops Code: ZBA ! ZBO + ZBV ZXQ #
Fishkind: "GRAMPUS" "RUDD" !

DB985683!	DB985817=(W)	DB985840 (W)	DB985858=(W)	DB985870
DB985701+(W)	DB985821=	DB985841 (W)	DB985859	DB985871
DB985728!	DB985822 (W)	DB985842	DB985860 (W)	DB985873
DB985743=	DB985828!	DB985843	DB985862 (W)	DB985874 (W)
DB985757+	DB985829=	DB985844=	DB985863 (W)	DB985875
DB985759+(W)	DB985832=(W)	DB985845 (W)	DB985864=	DB985876 (W)
DB985768#(W)	DB985833	DB985848=	DB985865=	DB985877=
DB985774!	DB985835	DB985850*(W)	DB985866=	DB985879!
DB985811 (W)	DB985836=	DB985853	DB985867 (W)	DB985881=
DB985814 (W)	DB985837=(W)	DB985856=	DB985869	DB985882=(W)
DB985815!	DB985839	DB985857		

Number Series: DB985953 - DB986125

Description: 20T Ballast & Sleeper Wagon
Builder: Butterley Engineering Co Ltd — Lot No.: 2884
Diagram No.: 1/572 — Built: 1956
Tare Weight: 9.1t + 10.5t — G.L.W.: 31.0t
Design Code: ZB501A + ZB501K ZB501M % — Tops Code: ZBA + ZBV
Fishkind: "GRAMPUS"

DB985953+	DB985998%(W)	DB986081 (W)	DB986100+	DB986125

Number Series: DB986160 - DB986251

Description: 20T Ballast & Sleeper Wagon
Builder: Gloucester R C & W Co Ltd — Lot No.: 2885
Diagram No.: 1/572 — Built: 1956
Tare Weight: 9.1t * 10.5t =+ 11.0t — G.L.W.: 30.5t 35.0t -
Design Code: ZB501G * ZB501K = ZB501U + ZB502B — Tops Code: ZBA ZBQ * ZBV =
Fishkind: "GRAMPUS" *= "HAKE" "RUDD" +

DB986160=	DB986179*	DB986208	DB986250+	DB986251

Number Series: DB986390 - DB986450

Description: 20T Ballast & Sleeper Wagon
Builder: Cambrian Wagon & Eng Co Ltd — Lot No.: 2886
Diagram No.: 1/572 — Built: 1956
Tare Weight: 9.1t + 10.5t — G.L.W.: 30.5t
Design Codes: ZB501A ZB501K = ZB501M % ZB501U * ZB501Y # — Tops Code: ZBA #* ZBO ZBV =%
Fishkind: "GRAMPUS" "RUDD" #*

DB986390	DB986413%	DB986437	DB986446#	DB986450*
DB986401=(W)				

Number Series: DB986465 - DB986552

Description: 20T Ballast & Sleeper Wagon
Builder: Derbyshire C & W Co Ltd — Lot No.: 2887
Diagram No: 1/572 — Built: 1956-57
Tare Weight: 9.1t 10.5t % — G.L.W.: 30.5t
Design Code: ZB501A ZB501Q # ZB501Y % — Tops Code: ZBA % ZBO
Fishkind: "GRAMPUS" "RUDD" #%

DB986465#	DB986480	DB986481	DB986492 (W)	DB986552%

Number Series: DB986566 - DB986689

Description: 20T Ballast & Sleeper Wagon
Builder: Butterley Engineering Co Ltd — Lot No.: 2777
Diagram No.: 1/572 — Built: 1955-56
Tare Weight: 9.1t * 10.5t — G.L.W.: 30.5t
Design Code: ZB501A ZB501K = ZB501M % ZB501Q # ZB501U * — Tops Code: ZBA * ZBO ZBV =%
Fishkind: "GRAMPUS" "RUDD" *

DB986566#	DB986603=(W)	DB986657 (W)	DB986671%(W)	DB986689*

Number Series: DB986718 - DB986772

Description: 20T Ballast & Sleeper Wagon
Builder: Cambrian Wagon & Eng Co Ltd — Lot No.: 2778
Diagram No.: 1/572 — Built: 1955
Tare Weight: 10.5t — G.L.W.: 10.5t
Design Code: ZB501A ZB501M % — Tops Code: ZBO ZBV %
Fishkind: "GRAMPUS"

DB986718 (W)	DB986731%(W)	DB986763	DB986767%(W)	DB986772%(W)

Number Series: DB986839 - DB986958

Description: 20T Ballast & Sleeper Wagon
Builder: Gloucester R C & W Co Ltd — Lot No.: 2780
Diagram No.: 1/572 — Built: 1955-56
Tare Weight: 9.1t * 10.5t — G.L.W.: 30.5t
Design Code: ZB501A ZB501K = ZB501M % ZB501Q # ZB501U * — Tops Code: ZBA * ZBO ZBV =%
Fishkind: "GRAMPUS" "RUDD" *

DB986839	DB986858=(W)	DB986886	DB986933*	DB986958%
DB986840#	DB986859 (W)	DB986913	DB986946*	

Number Series: DB986962

Description: 20T Ballast & Sleeper Wagon
Builder: Gloucester R C & W Co Ltd — Lot No.: 3051
Diagram No.: 1/572 — Built: 1957
Tare Weight: 10.5t — G.L.W.: 30.5t
Design Code: ZB501M — Tops Code: ZBV
Fishkind: "GRAMPUS"

DB986962 (W)

Number Series: DB987101 - DB987104

Description: 22T Ballast & Sleeper Wagon
Builder: BR (Horwich Works) — Lot No.: 3929
Diagram No.: 1/432 — Built: 1978
Tare Weight: 10.15t — G.L.W.: 33.0t
Design Code: ZC002A ZC002B * — Tops Code: ZCV
Fishkind: "PLAICE"

DB987101* DB987102* DB987103 DB987104

Number Series: DB987105 - DB987305

Description: 22T Ballast & Sleeper Wagon
Builder: BR (Horwich Works) — Lot No.: 3970
Diagram No.: 1/432 — Built: 1979-80
Tare Weight: 10.15t — G.L.W.: 32.5t
Design Code: ZC511A ZC511B * — Tops Code: ZCV
Fishkind: "PLAICE"

DB987105
DB987106
DB987107
DB987108
DB987109
DB987110
DB987111
DB987112
DB987113
DB987114
DB987115
DB987116
DB987117
DB987118*
DB987119
DB987120
DB987121
DB987122
DB987123
DB987124
DB987125
DB987126
DB987127
DB987128
DB987129
DB987130
DB987131
DB987132
DB987133
DB987134
DB987135
DB987136
DB987137
DB987138
DB987139
DB987140
DB987141
DB987142
DB987143
DB987144
DB987145
DB987146
DB987147
DB987148
DB987149 (W)
DB987150
DB987151 (W)
DB987152
DB987153
DB987154
DB987156
DB987157 (W)
DB987158
DB987159
DB987160
DB987161
DB987162
DB987163
DB987164
DB987165 (W)
DB987166
DB987167
DB987168
DB987169
DB987170
DB987171 (W)
DB987172
DB987173
DB987174
DB987175
DB987176
DB987177
DB987178
DB987179
DB987180
DB987181
DB987182
DB987183 (W)
DB987185 (W)
DB987186
DB987187
DB987188
DB987189
DB987190
DB987191
DB987192
DB987193 (W)
DB987194
DB987195
DB987196
DB987197
DB987198
DB987199
DB987200
DB987201
DB987202
DB987203
DB987204
DB987205
DB987207
DB987208
DB987209
DB987210
DB987211
DB987212
DB987213
DB987214
DB987215
DB987216
DB987217
DB987218
DB987219
DB987220
DB987221
DB987222
DB987223
DB987224
DB987225
DB987226
DB987227
DB987228
DB987229
DB987230
DB987231 (W)
DB987232

DB987233
DB987234
DB987235
DB987236
DB987237
DB987238
DB987239
DB987240
DB987241 (W)
DB987242
DB987243
DB987244
DB987245
DB987246
DB987247
DB987248
DB987249
DB987250
DB987251
DB987252
DB987253
DB987254
DB987255
DB987256
DB987257
DB987258
DB987259
DB987260
DB987261
DB987262
DB987263
DB987264
DB987266
DB987267
DB987268
DB987269
DB987270
DB987271
DB987272
DB987273
DB987274
DB987275
DB987276
DB987277
DB987278 (W)
DB987279
DB987280
DB987281
DB987282
DB987283
DB987284
DB987285 (W)
DB987286
DB987287
DB987288
DB987289
DB987290
DB987291
DB987292
DB987293
DB987294
DB987295
DB987298
DB987299
DB987300
DB987301
DB987302
DB987303
DB987304
DB987305*

<u>Number Series: DB988200 - DB988418</u>

Description: 20T Ballast & Sleeper Wagon
Builder: BR (Horwich Works)
Diagram No.: 1/572
Tare Weight: 10.5t
Design Code: ZB501B ZB501M * ZB501P =
ZB501R % ZB501X : ZC013C #
ZC013D !
Fishkind: "GRAMPUS" "EGRET" #!

Lot No.: 3245
Built: 1959-60
G.L.W.: 30.5t * 31.0t
Tops Code: ZBV

DB988200=
DB988202=
DB988203
DB988204
DB988205=(W)
DB988206
DB988207!
DB988208=
DB988209*
DB988210 (W)
DB988211*
DB988212=
DB988213
DB988214
DB988215=
DB988218=
DB988219=
DB988220=
DB988221=
DB988222=
DB988223=
DB988225=
DB988227=(W)
DB988228
DB988229=
DB988230
DB988231=
DB988233
DB988235=
DB988237=
DB988238=(W)
DB988239
DB988240!
DB988241
DB988242=
DB988243%(W)
DB988245
DB988246=
DB988247=
DB988248
DB988249
DB988250=
DB988251%(W)
DB988252
DB988253*(W)
DB988254
DB988255=
DB988256
DB988257
DB988258=
DB988259
DB988260=
DB988261=
DB988262%
DB988263=
DB988264%
DB988265*
DB988266=(W)
DB988267%
DB988271=(W)
DB988272%
DB988274%
DB988275=
DB988276=(W)
DB988277
DB988278=
DB988279%
DB988280=(W)
DB988281=
DB988283=
DB988284
DB988288+
DB988289=(W)
DB988290=
DB988291=
DB988292*
DB988293
DB988295=
DB988296=
DB988297=
DB988300
DB988301
DB988302=
DB988303=
DB988304=
DB988305
DB988306=
DB988307=
DB988308=
DB988309
DB988310
DB988311
DB988312=
DB988313 (W)
DB988314 (W)
DB988315%(W)
DB988316=
DB988319=
DB988320=
DB988321=
DB988322=
DB988324=
DB988325*(W)
DB988326
DB988327
DB988328
DB988329
DB988331=
DB988333=
DB988335
DB988336=
DB988337*
DB988338=
DB988339=(W)
DB988340
DB988341=
DB988342=
DB988345=
DB988346=
DB988348
DB988349*
DB988352
DB988353
DB988354%(W)
DB988355
DB988356=
DB988357=
DB988358=
DB988359=
DB988361=
DB988363
DB988365
DB988366=
DB988368
DB988370=
DB988371 (W)
DB988372=
DB988373
DB988374%(W)
DB988375
DB988376
DB988377=
DB988378
DB988379=
DB988381%
DB988382=
DB988383=
DB988384=
DB988387*
DB988388
DB988389=
DB988390=
DB988391=
DB988393=(W)
DB988394=
DB988396=
DB988397
DB988398=(W)
DB988399=
DB988400#

DB988401
DB988402=
DB988403*
DB988406
DB988407=
DB988409 (W)
DB988410:
DB988411
DB988412=
DB988413=
DB988415
DB988416 (W)
DB988417
DB988418

Number Series: DB988420 - DB988520

Description: 20T Ballast & Sleeper Wagon
Builder: BR (Shildon Works)
Diagram No.: 1/572
Tare Weight: 10.5t
Design Code: ZB501C ZB501L * ZB501S =
ZS013E #
Fishkind: "GRAMPUS" "EGRET" #

Lot No.: 3282
Built: 1960
G.L.W.: 31.0t
Tops Code: ZBV

DB988420
DB988421*
DB988423*
DB988424*
DB988426*
DB988427
DB988428*
DB988430
DB988432*
DB988433
DB988434*
DB988435*
DB988436*
DB988437=
DB988438
DB988439
DB988440
DB988441
DB988442#
DB988443*
DB988444*(W)
DB988447 (W)
DB988448
DB988449*
DB988450*
DB988451*(W)
DB988452*
DB988453*
DB988454*
DB988455 (W)
DB988458
DB988460*
DB988461
DB988462*
DB988463
DB988464=
DB988465
DB988466*
DB988467
DB988469*
DB988470
DB988472*
DB988473=
DB988476
DB988477*
DB988478*
DB988479=(W)
DB988480*
DB988482
DB988483*
DB988484*
DB988485*
DB988486*
DB988487
DB988488*
DB988489*
DB988490
DB988492*
DB988493
DB988496*
DB988497
DB988498*
DB988499 (W)
DB988500*
DB988501
DB988502*
DB988503*
DB988504*
DB988505*
DB988506*
DB988507*
DB988508=(W)
DB988509*
DB988510
DB988511*
DB988512*
DB988513*
DB988514
DB988516*
DB988517 (W)
DB988518*
DB988519 (W)
DB988520*

Number Series: DB988522 - DB988594

Description: 20T Ballast & Sleeper Wagon
Builder: BR (Shildon Works)
Diagram No.: 1/572
Tare Weight: 10.5t
Design Code: ZB501C + ZB501L * ZB501S =
Fishkind: "GRAMPUS"

Lot No.: 3339
Built: 1960
G.L.W.: 31.0t
Tops Code: ZBV

DB988522*
DB988523
DB988524*
DB988526
DB988528*
DB988529
DB988532*
DB988533*
DB988534 (W)
DB988535
DB988536*
DB988537 (W)
DB988539*
DB988540*
DB988541*
DB988542*
DB988543*
DB988544*(W)
DB988545*
DB988546
DB988547*
DB988548
DB988549*
DB988550=
DB988551*
DB988552*(W)
DB988553*
DB988554=
DB988555=
DB988557*
DB988558*
DB988560*(W)
DB988561*
DB988562*
DB988563*(W)
DB988564
DB988565*(W)
DB988566*(W)
DB988567*
DB988569=(W)
DB988570*
DB988573=
DB988574=
DB988575
DB988576*(W)
DB988577*(W)
DB988578*
DB988580=(W)
DB988582=(W)
DB988583 (W)
DB988584*
DB988585*
DB988586=
DB988587=
DB988589=(W)
DB988590=(W)
DB988591*(W)
DB988592=(W)
DB988593*(W)
DB988594*(W)

Number Series: DB988600

Description: 27T Ballast Wagon
Builder: BR (Shildon Works) — Lot No.: 4032
Tare Weight: 13.0t — Built: 1983
Design Code: ZB503A — G.L.W.: 40.0t
Fishkind: "CARP" — Tops Code: ZBA

DB988600

Number Series: DB989000 - DB989019

Description: 14T Side Tipping Ballast Wagon
Builder: Metropolitan Cammell Co Ltd — Lot No.: 2428
Diagram No.: 1/573 — Built: 1954
Tare Weight: 11.1t — G.L.W.: 24.0t
Design Code: ZJ500C — Tops Code: ZJV
Fishkind: "MERMAID"

DB989000	DB989003	DB989007	DB989011	DB989017 (W)
DB989001	DB989004	DB989009	DB989013	DB989018
DB989002	DB989006 (W)	DB989010	DB989014	DB989019

Number Series: DB989022 - DB989067

Description: 14T Side Tipping Ballast Wagon
Builder: Metropolitan Cammell Co Ltd — Lot No.: 2535
Diagram No.: 1/573 — Built: 1955
Tare Weight: 11.1t — G.L.W.: 24.0t
Design Code: ZJ500C — Tops Code: ZJV
Fishkind: "MERMAID"

DB989022 (W)	DB989036 (W)	DB989048	DB989054	DB989061
DB989024	DB989041	DB989050 (W)	DB989055	DB989062
DB989026	DB989043	DB989051	DB989056	DB989063
DB989028	DB989046	DB989052	DB989058	DB989065
DB989031 (W)	DB989047	DB989053 (W)	DB989060	DB989067

Number Series: DB989073 - DB989088

Description: 14T Side Tipping Ballast Wagon
Builder: Metropolitan Cammell Co Ltd — Lot No.: 2928
Diagram No.: 1/573 — Built: 1957
Tare Weight: 11.1t — G.L.W.: 24.0t
Design Code: ZJ500C — Tops Code: ZJV
Fishkind: "MERMAID"

DB989073	DB989076	DB989079	DB989084	DB989087
DB989074 (W)	DB989078	DB989081	DB989086	DB989088

Number Series: DB989089 - DB989234

Description: 14T Side Tipping Ballast Wagon
Builder: Metropolitan Cammell Co Ltd
Lot No.: 3170
Diagram No.: 1/575
Built: 1959-60
Tare Weight: 11.1t
G.L.W.: 25.0t
Design Code: ZJ500B
Tops Code: ZJV
Fishkind: "MERMAID"

DB989089	DB989117	DB989150	DB989184	DB989209
DB989090	DB989118	DB989151 (W)	DB989185 (W)	DB989210 (W)
DB989094	DB989119	DB989152	DB989186 (W)	DB989211
DB989095	DB989120	DB989153	DB989187	DB989212 (W)
DB989096	DB989122	DB989155	DB989188	DB989214
DB989097	DB989123	DB989157	DB989189	DB989216
DB989098	DB989128	DB989162 (W)	DB989190	DB989217 (W)
DB989100	DB989129	DB989163	DB989192	DB989221 (W)
DB989102	DB989130	DB989165	DB989193	DB989223 (W)
DB989103	DB989132	DB989166	DB989196	DB989225
DB989104	DB989134	DB989168	DB989197	DB989226 (W)
DB989105	DB989135	DB989169	DB989200	DB989227
DB989106	DB989138	DB989170	DB989201	DB989229
DB989107	DB989139	DB989171 (W)	DB989202	DB989230
DB989108	DB989141	DB989173	DB989203	DB989231
DB989111	DB989144 (W)	DB989176 (W)	DB989204	DB989232
DB989112 (W)	DB989147	DB989178	DB989205	DB989233 (W)
DB989115	DB989148	DB989180	DB989207 (W)	DB989234
DB989116 (W)	DB989149	DB989183	DB989208	

Number Series: DB989239 - DB989288

Description: 14T Side Tipping Ballast Wagon
Builder: Metropolitan Cammell Co Ltd
Lot No.: 3256
Diagram No.: 1/575
Built: 1959-60
Tare Weight: 11.1t
G.L.W.: 25.0t
Design Code: ZJ500B
Tops Code: ZJV
Fishkind: "MERMAID"

DB989239	DB989250	DB989259	DB989268 (W)	DB989276
DB989242	DB989251	DB989260	DB989270	DB989279
DB989243	DB989252	DB989262	DB989271	DB989281
DB989245 (W)	DB989253 (W)	DB989263 (W)	DB989272	DB989282
DB989246	DB989254	DB989265	DB989273 (W)	DB989283
DB989247	DB989255	DB989266	DB989274	DB989284
DB989248	DB989256	DB989267 (W)	DB989275	DB989288
DB989249	DB989258			

Number Series: DB989289 - DB989588

Description: 14T Side Tipping Ballast Wagon
Builder: Metropolitan Cammell Co Ltd
Lot No.: 3330
Diagram No.: 1/575
Built: 1960-61
Tare Weight: 11.1t
G.L.W.: 25.0t
Design Code: ZJ500B
Tops Code: ZJV
Fishkind: "MERMAID"

DB989289
DB989290
DB989291
DB989292
DB989294
DB989295
DB989296
DB989297
DB989298
DB989299 (W)
DB989301
DB989302
DB989303
DB989304
DB989305
DB989307
DB989308
DB989310
DB989312 (W)
DB989313
DB989314
DB989316
DB989317
DB989321
DB989322
DB989324 (W)
DB989325 (W)
DB989326
DB989327
DB989328
DB989329
DB989330
DB989331
DB989332
DB989333
DB989334 (W)
DB989336
DB989337 (W)
DB989338 (W)
DB989339
DB989340
DB989341
DB989343
DB989344
DB989347 (W)
DB989348 (W)
DB989349
DB989350
DB989352
DB989353
DB989354
DB989355
DB989362
DB989363 (W)
DB989364
DB989365
DB989366
DB989368 (W)
DB989370
DB989372
DB989373
DB989374 (W)
DB989375
DB989376
DB989377
DB989378
DB989382
DB989383
DB989385
DB989386
DB989389 (W)
DB989391
DB989395
DB989396
DB989397
DB989398
DB989399
DB989400
DB989402
DB989403
DB989404
DB989406
DB989407
DB989409
DB989410
DB989411
DB989412
DB989413
DB989415
DB989416
DB989417
DB989418
DB989419
DB989422
DB989426
DB989428
DB989430
DB989432
DB989434
DB989435
DB989436
DB989437
DB989438
DB989439
DB989440
DB989441
DB989443
DB989445
DB989446
DB989447
DB989449
DB989450
DB989451
DB989452
DB989453
DB989454
DB989455 (W)
DB989456
DB989457
DB989458
DB989460
DB989461
DB989462
DB989463
DB989464
DB989465
DB989467
DB989468
DB989469
DB989470
DB989471
DB989472
DB989473
DB989474
DB989476
DB989477
DB989478
DB989479 (W)
DB989480
DB989481
DB989482
DB989483
DB989485
DB989487
DB989488
DB989489
DB989492
DB989494
DB989495 (W)
DB989496
DB989498
DB989499
DB989500
DB989501
DB989502
DB989503
DB989506
DB989507
DB989508
DB989509
DB989510
DB989511
DB989512
DB989513
DB989514
DB989515
DB989517
DB989518
DB989519
DB989520
DB989522
DB989523
DB989524
DB989525
DB989527
DB989528
DB989529
DB989530
DB989532 (W)
DB989533
DB989534
DB989535
DB989536
DB989540
DB989541
DB989543
DB989544
DB989545
DB989546
DB989547
DB989549
DB989551
DB989552
DB989553
DB989554
DB989556
DB989557
DB989558
DB989559
DB989560
DB989562
DB989563
DB989564
DB989566
DB989568
DB989570
DB989571
DB989572
DB989574
DB989575
DB989577
DB989578
DB989579
DB989580
DB989581
DB989582
DB989583
DB989584
DB989585
DB989586
DB989588

Number Series: DB989589 - DB989638

Description: 14T Side Tipping Ballast Wagon
Builder: BR (Shildon Works)
Lot No.: 3339
Diagram No.: 1/575
Built: 1961
Tare Weight: 11.1t
G.L.W.: 25.0t
Design Code: ZJ500B
Tops Code: ZJV
Fishkind: "MERMAID"

DB989589
DB989590
DB989591
DB989592
DB989593
DB989594
DB989595
DB989598
DB989599
DB989600
DB989601
DB989602 (W)
DB989603
DB989604
DB989605

DB989606	DB989613	DB989620	DB989627	DB989633
DB989607	DB989614	DB989621	DB989628	DB989634
DB989608	DB989615	DB989622	DB989629	DB989635
DB989609	DB989616	DB989623	DB989630	DB989636
DB989610	DB989617	DB989624 (W)	DB989631	DB989637
DB989611	DB989618	DB989625	DB989632	DB989638
DB989612	DB989619	DB989626		

Number Series: DB990113 - DB990393

Description: 21T Ballast & Sleeper Wagon
Builder: BR (Shildon Works) Lot No.: 2200
Diagram No.: 1/572 Built: 1951-52
Tare Weight: 9.1t 10.5t =#* G.L.W.: 30.5t
Design Codes: ZB501A ZB501M = ZB501U # ZB501Y * Tops Code: ZBA #* ZBO ZBV =
Fishkind: "GRAMPUS" "RUDD" #*

DB990113	DB990231=	DB990295	DB990371*	DB990393#
DB990191	DB990271=(W)	DB990368=	DB990382=	

Number Series: DB990444 - DB990687

Description: 21T Ballast & Sleeper Wagon
Builder: BR (Shildon Works) Lot No.: 2345
Diagram No.: 1/572 Built: 1953
Tare Weight: 9.1t + 10.5t G.L.W.: 30.5t
Design Codes: ZB501A + ZB501K ZB501M = ZB501T ! ZB501U * Tops Code: ZBA * ZBO + ZBV
Fishkind: "GRAMPUS" "RUDD" *

DB990444+	DB990518 (W)	DB990536 (W)	DB990546+	DB990576 (W)
DB990458=	DB990520 (W)	DB990538	DB990548 (W)	DB990577
DB990510=(W)	DB990524 (W)	DB990539 (W)	DB990550=	DB990630*
DB990512 (W)	DB990526	DB990541!(W)	DB990551=	DB990654
DB990513 (W)	DB990527=	DB990542 (W)	DB990554 (W)	DB990655=
DB990514=(W)	DB990528=(W)	DB990543=	DB990571 (W)	DB990663+
DB990515=	DB990530=(W)	DB990545	DB990574	DB990687*
DB990516=	DB990534 (W)			

Number Series: DB990690 - DB990853

Description: 21T Ballast & Sleeper Wagon
Builder: Cambrian Wagon & Eng Co Ltd Lot No.: 2940
Diagram No.: 1/572 Built: 1957
Tare Weight: 9.1t + 10.5t G.L.W.: 30.5t
Design Codes: ZB501A + ZB501K % ZB501M ZB501T ! ZB501Y * Tops Code: ZBA * ZBO + ZBV
Fishkind: "GRAMPUS" "RUDD" *

DB990690+	DB990707+	DB990742%	DB990770*	DB990853!
DB990702+	DB990709+	DB990761 (W)	DB990839	

Number Series: DB990885 - DB990956

Description: 21T Ballast & Sleeper Wagon
Builder: Derbyshire C & W Co Ltd — Lot No.: 2941
Diagram No.: 1/572 — Built: 1957
Tare Weight: 9.1t + 10.5t — G.L.W.: 30.5t
Design Code: ZB501A + ZB501K % ZB501M — Tops Code: ZBO + ZBV
Fishkind: "GRAMPUS"

DB990885%	DB990909+(W)	DB990936	DB990947 (W)	DB990952
DB990894+(W)	DB990912+	DB990944	DB990948%	DB990956 (W)
DB990906+	DB990926+	DB990945		

Number Series: DB991000 - DB991020

Description: 20T Ballast Wagon
Builder: BR (Lancing Works) — Lot No.: 2065
Diagram No.: 1/570 — Built: 1951
Tare Weight: 9.75t — G.L.W.: 30.0t
Design Code: ZC513B — Tops Code: ZCV
Fishkind: "CRAB"

DB991000	DB991004	DB991010	DB991015	DB991019
DB991002	DB991005	DB991011	DB991017	DB991020
DB991003	DB991007	DB991013		

Number Series: DB991151 - DB991299

Description: 20T Ballast Wagon
Builder: Butterley Engineering Co Ltd — Lot No.: 2241
Diagram No.: 1/570 — Built: 1951-52
Tare Weight: 9.1t # 9.75t — G.L.W.: 30.0t 30.5t #+
Design Code: ZB500A # ZB500E + ZC513B — Tops Code: ZBV ZBO +#
Fishkind "LAMPREY" #+ "CRAB"

DB991151+	DB991254	DB991266	DB991280	DB991290
DB991172	DB991256 (W)	DB991267	DB991281	DB991291
DB991204	DB991258	DB991270	DB991285	DB991292
DB991243 (W)	DB991261	DB991272	DB991287	DB991294
DB991244 (W)	DB991263	DB991275#	DB991288	DB991295
DB991249	DB991264	DB991276	DB991289 (W)	DB991299
DB991250	DB991265	DB991278		

Number Series: DB991301 - DB991320

Description: 20T Ballast Wagon
Builder: BR (Lancing Works) — Lot No.: 2102
Diagram No.: 1/570 — Built: 1951
Tare Weight: 9.75t — G.L.W. 30.0t
Design Code: ZC513B — Tops Code: ZCV
Fishkind: "CRAB"

DB991301	DB991303	DB991305	DB991307	DB991309
DB991302	DB991304	DB991306	DB991308	DB991310

DB991312	DB991315	DB991317	DB991319	DB991320
DB991313	DB991316 (W)	DB991318		

Number Series: DB991321 - DB991864

Description: 20T Ballast & Sleeper Wagon
Builder: Pressed Steel Co Ltd — Lot No.: 3168
Diagram No.: 1/574 — Built: 1959
Tare Weight: 10.5t — G.L.W.: 31.0t
Design Code: ZB501C ZB501L * ZB501S + ZC013E # — Tops Code: ZBV
Fishkind: "GRAMPUS" "EGRET" #

DB991321	DB991381 (W)	DB991433*	DB991483*	DB991550
DB991322*	DB991382*	DB991434	DB991484	DB991552*
DB991323*	DB991383*	DB991435	DB991485+(W)	DB991553*
DB991324*	DB991384	DB991436*	DB991486#	DB991554*
DB991326	DB991385*	DB991437*	DB991487	DB991555
DB991330 (W)	DB991386	DB991438*	DB991488*	DB991556*
DB991331	DB991387 (W)	DB991439*	DB991489*	DB991557*
DB991332 (W)	DB991388*	DB991440*(W)	DB991490*(W)	DB991558*
DB991334*	DB991389	DB991441	DB991491	DB991559
DB991335*	DB991390 (W)	DB991442	DB991492*(W)	DB991561*
DB991336*	DB991392	DB991443*	DB991493+	DB991562 (W)
DB991337*	DB991393*	DB991444*	DB991494*(W)	DB991563*(W)
DB991338 (W)	DB991394*	DB991445*	DB991495	DB991565*
DB991340	DB991395*(W)	DB991446	DB991496 (W)	DB991566*
DB991341*	DB991396*	DB991447	DB991497*(W)	DB991567*
DB991342*	DB991398	DB991448*	DB991498*(W)	DB991568*
DB991344	DB991399*	DB991449	DB991500	DB991569*
DB991345	DB991402	DB991450	DB991502*(W)	DB991570*(W)
DB991346	DB991403*	DB991452	DB991504*(W)	DB991571*
DB991347	DB991405	DB991453	DB991507*(W)	DB991572
DB991348	DB991406*	DB991454	DB991508*	DB991573
DB991350*	DB991407*	DB991456	DB991509*	DB991574*
DB991352*	DB991408	DB991457	DB991512*(W)	DB991575*(W)
DB991354*(W)	DB991409*	DB991458	DB991514*(W)	DB991576*
DB991355*	DB991410	DB991459*	DB991515*	DB991577*
DB991356*	DB991411	DB991460	DB991519*(W)	DB991578 (W)
DB991358	DB991412	DB991461	DB991520*	DB991579*
DB991359*	DB991413*	DB991462	DB991521*(W)	DB991580*(W)
DB991361	DB991414	DB991463*	DB991522	DB991581*
DB991362	DB991415*(W)	DB991464	DB991523*	DB991582*(W)
DB991363	DB991416	DB991465	DB991524	DB991583
DB991364*	DB991417*	DB991466	DB991530*	DB991584*
DB991365*	DB991418	DB991468*(W)	DB991531 (W)	DB991585*
DB991366*	DB991419*	DB991469*(W)	DB991532*	DB991586*
DB991369 (W)	DB991420	DB991471*	DB991534*(W)	DB991588*
DB991370	DB991422	DB991472 (W)	DB991535*(W)	DB991589*(W)
DB991371*(W)	DB991423*	DB991473*	DB991536	DB991590
DB991372*	DB991424*	DB991474*(W)	DB991538*	DB991591 (W)
DB991373	DB991425	DB991475*	DB991539*(W)	DB991592
DB991374	DB991426	DB991476	DB991542*	DB991593*(W)
DB991375	DB991427	DB991477	DB991544*(W)	DB991594
DB991376	DB991428*	DB991479*	DB991545	DB991595
DB991377 (W)	DB991429*	DB991480*	DB991546	DB991596
DB991379*	DB991430	DB991481	DB991547*	DB991597*
DB991380*	DB991432+(W)	DB991482	DB991549	DB991598*(W)

DB991599*
DB991600
DB991601
DB991603*
DB991604*
DB991605*
DB991606*
DB991607*(W)
DB991609 (W)
DB991610
DB991611
DB991612*(W)
DB991613*(W)
DB991616*
DB991617*
DB991618*
DB991619*
DB991620*(W)
DB991622*
DB991623*(W)
DB991625
DB991626*
DB991628*
DB991629*
DB991630*
DB991631
DB991632
DB991634*
DB991635*(W)
DB991636*
DB991637
DB991638
DB991640*
DB991641*
DB991642*
DB991643*
DB991644*
DB991645
DB991647*
DB991648*
DB991649
DB991650
DB991651
DB991652+(W)
DB991653
DB991654
DB991655*(W)
DB991658
DB991659
DB991660 (W)
DB991661*
DB991662 (W)
DB991663*
DB991664
DB991665*
DB991666
DB991667*
DB991668*(W)
DB991670*(W)
DB991671 (W)
DB991672
DB991673
DB991674*
DB991675*
DB991676*
DB991677
DB991678
DB991679*
DB991680*
DB991681
DB991682*
DB991683*
DB991684
DB991685*
DB991686*
DB991687
DB991688*
DB991690*
DB991692
DB991693*
DB991696*
DB991697*
DB991698*
DB991699*
DB991700
DB991701*
DB991702*
DB991703*
DB991704*
DB991706
DB991707*
DB991709*
DB991711*
DB991712
DB991713*(W)
DB991714
DB991715*
DB991716*
DB991717*
DB991718
DB991719
DB991721*
DB991722*
DB991723
DB991724
DB991725
DB991726*
DB991727
DB991728+
DB991729
DB991732
DB991733*(W)
DB991734
DB991736
DB991737*
DB991738*
DB991739*(W)
DB991740*
DB991742 (W)
DB991743*
DB991744
DB991745*
DB991746*
DB991747*
DB991748*
DB991749*
DB991750
DB991751
DB991752*
DB991753+(W)
DB991754*
DB991755*
DB991756*
DB991758+
DB991759*
DB991760*
DB991761
DB991762*
DB991763
DB991764*
DB991765*
DB991766*
DB991767
DB991768*
DB991769*
DB991770*
DB991771*
DB991772*
DB991773*
DB991775*
DB991776
DB991778
DB991780*
DB991781*
DB991782*
DB991783*
DB991784*
DB991785*
DB991786*
DB991787
DB991788*
DB991789 (W)
DB991790*
DB991791*(W)
DB991792*
DB991793
DB991794*(W)
DB991795
DB991796*
DB991797*
DB991798*
DB991799*
DB991800*(W)
DB991801*(W)
DB991802*(W)
DB991803*
DB991804*
DB991806 (W)
DB991807*
DB991808*
DB991809*
DB991810
DB991811
DB991812*(W)
DB991813
DB991814*
DB991815
DB991816*(W)
DB991817*
DB991818
DB991819*
DB991820*
DB991821+(W)
DB991822*
DB991823
DB991825*
DB991826*
DB991827*
DB991828*
DB991829*
DB991830*
DB991831
DB991832
DB991833*(W)
DB991834*
DB991835*
DB991836
DB991837*
DB991838*
DB991839*
DB991840
DB991841*
DB991843
DB991844*
DB991845*
DB991846*
DB991847+(W)
DB991848
DB991849*
DB991850*
DB991851*
DB991852
DB991853
DB991854*
DB991855*
DB991856
DB991857*
DB991858
DB991859
DB991861*
DB991862*
DB991863
DB991864 (W)

<u>Number Series: DB992419 - DB992461</u>

Description: 20T Ballast Hopper Wagon
Builder: Metropolitan Cammell Co Ltd
Lot No.: 2405
Diagram No.: 1/584
Built: 1952-54
Tare Weight: 9.8t
G.L.W.: 30.5t
Design Code: ZL501A
Tops Code: ZLV
Fishkind: "HERRING"

DB992419
DB992444
DB992461

Number Series: DB992506 - DB992521

Description: 40T Bogie Ballast Hopper Wagon
Builder: Metropolitan Cammell Co Ltd
Diagram No.: 1/585
Tare Weight: 21.5t
Design Code: YG500C YG500J +
Fishkind: "WALRUS"

Lot No.: 2411
Built: 1954
G.L.W.: 62.0t
Tops Code: YGV

DB992506+(W)	DB992518 (W)	DB992521 (W)

Number Series: DB992533 - DB992590

Description: 19T Ballast Hopper Wagon
Builder: Metropolitan Cammell Co Ltd
Diagram No.: 1/586
Tare Weight: 9.8t
Design Code: ZE500A + ZE500B
Fishkind: "CATFISH"

Lot No.: 2682
Built: 1955
G.L.W.: 30.0t
Tops Code: ZEV

DB992533+	DB992546+	DB992555	DB992569	DB992581
DB992534	DB992547	DB992556	DB992571	DB992583
DB992535	DB992548+	DB992557	DB992572	DB992585
DB992537	DB992549	DB992559+	DB992575+	DB992586
DB992538+	DB992550	DB992560+	DB992576	DB992587
DB992540	DB992551	DB992563	DB992578	DB992588+
DB992542	DB992552	DB992565	DB992579+	DB992589+
DB992544	DB992553	DB992566+	DB992580	DB992590+
DB992545	DB992554			

Number Series: DB992591 - DB992650

Description: 19T Ballast Hopper Wagon
Builder: Metropolitan Cammell Co Ltd
Diagram No.: 1/586
Tare Weight: 9.8t
Design Code: ZE500A ZE500B + ZE500C #
ZS152B *

Lot No.: 2683
Built: 1955
G.L.W.: 9.8t * 30.0t
Tops Code: ZEV ZSV *
Fishkind: "CATFISH"

DB992591	DB992606+	DB992615+	DB992625	DB992636+
DB992594+	DB992608+	DB992616+	DB992627+	DB992638+
DB992597+	DB992609	DB992617+	DB992630+	DB992641+
DB992599+	DB992610+	DB992618+	DB992631+	DB992644*
DB992602	DB992611+	DB992620	DB992633+	DB992648
DB992604+	DB992613#	DB992621+	DB992635+	DB992650+
DB992605+	DB992614+	DB992624+		

Number Series: DB992653 - DB992710

Description: 19T Ballast Hopper Wagon
Builder: Metropolitan Cammell Co Ltd
Diagram No.: 1/586
Tare Weight: 9.8t
Design Code: ZE500A + ZE500B
Fishkind: "CATFISH"

Lot No.: 2775
Built: 1955
G.L.W.: 30.0t
Tops Code: ZEV

DB992653	DB992667	DB992679	DB992691	DB992702
DB992657	DB992669+	DB992683	DB992692	DB992703
DB992658	DB992670	DB992684	DB992693	DB992704+
DB992659	DB992672+	DB992685	DB992696+	DB992706
DB992662	DB992673	DB992687+	DB992697	DB992707+
DB992663	DB992675	DB992689	DB992700+	DB992709
DB992665	DB992676+	DB992690	DB992701	DB992710+
DB992666+				

Number Series: DB992711 - DB992858

Description: 24T Ballast Hopper Wagon
Builder: Charles Roberts Ltd
Diagram No.: 1/587
Tare Weight: 11.5t 11.8t # 12.0t +
Design Code: ZF501A * ZF501B ZF501C #
ZF501F +

Lot No.: 2819
Built: 1956
G.L.W.: 36.5t
Tops Code: ZFV ZFW +
Fishkind: "DOGFISH"

DB992711	DB992739*	DB992768	DB992798#	DB992827#
DB992712	DB992740	DB992769	DB992800	DB992829#
DB992713	DB992741	DB992770#	DB992801	DB992832#
DB992714	DB992742	DB992771	DB992802	DB992833#
DB992715	DB992743	DB992772#	DB992803	DB992834#
DB992716	DB992744*	DB992773	DB992804#	DB992836#
DB992718	DB992745	DB992774#	DB992805	DB992839#
DB992719	DB992746	DB992776#	DB992806	DB992840#
DB992721	DB992747 (W)	DB992777#	DB992807	DB992843
DB992722	DB992749	DB992779#	DB992809#	DB992844#
DB992724	DB992750	DB992780#	DB992811#	DB992845
DB992725+	DB992751	DB992781	DB992812	DB992846#
DB992726	DB992752	DB992782#	DB992813#	DB992848
DB992727	DB992753	DB992783#	DB992815	DB992849#
DB992728	DB992754+	DB992785#	DB992817#	DB992850#
DB992729	DB992757	DB992787#	DB992818#	DB992851
DB992730	DB992759	DB992790	DB992820#	DB992852#
DB992731	DB992760*	DB992791	DB992821*	DB992853#(W)
DB992732	DB992762	DB992792#	DB992822	DB992854
DB992733	DB992763	DB992794#	DB992823	DB992855#
DB992734	DB992764*	DB992795	DB992824#	DB992856#
DB992735	DB992765#	DB992796	DB992825	DB992857
DB992736	DB992767	DB992797	DB992826#	DB992858#
DB992738*				

ZCV, "Plaice", DB987216, a 22T Ballast & Sleeper Wagon, is pictured at Bescot on 4th September 1993. Peter Ifold

ZBV, "Crab", DB991244, a 20T Ballast Wagon, was withdrawn when seen at Eastleigh on 27th March 1994. Originally a "Lamprey" this wagon along with many others were subject to modifications and reclassified as "Crab". Peter Ifold

ZFV, "Dogfish", DB992849, a 24T Ballast Hopper Wagon, is seen at Mossend on 30th July 1989. Paul W. Bartlett

One of only two remaining examples in use on BR, ZUP, "Oyster", DB993706, a 16T Ballast Brake Van, is pictured at Bescot on 5th September 1992. Paul W. Bartlett

Photographed at Perth on 1st August 1989 when in service, YBQ, "Sturgeon", DB994176 a 50T Bogie Ballast Wagon was withdrawn prior to June 1993 although many of its companions survive. Paul W. Bartlett

YMA, "Salmon", DB996483, a 50T Bogie Rail Wagon, is seen at Woking on 26th March 1994. Peter Ifold

Photographed at Eastleigh on 27th March 1994 is YFA, "Salmon", DB996637, a 50T Bogie Rail Wagon. Peter Ifold

ZVR, "Loriot", DB998018, a 20T Flatrol Wagon, is pictured complete with load at Woking on 26th March 1994. Peter Ifold

Number Series: DB992859 - DB993058

Description: 24T Ballast Hopper Wagon
Builder: Metropolitan Cammell Co Ltd
Diagram No.: 1/587
Tare Weight: 11.5t 11.8t # 12.0t +
Design Code: ZF501A * ZF501B ZF501C #
ZF501F +

Lot No.: 2820
Built: 1956-57
G.L.W.: 36.5t
Tops Code: ZFV ZFW +
Fishkind: "DOGFISH"

DB992859	DB992894	DB992936	DB992983	DB993024
DB992860	DB992895	DB992937*	DB992985#	DB993025
DB992861	DB992896	DB992940	DB992987	DB993027*
DB992862	DB992898	DB992941	DB992988	DB993028*
DB992864	DB992899	DB992942	DB992989	DB993029
DB992865	DB992900	DB992943	DB992990	DB993031
DB992866	DB992901*	DB992944*	DB992991#	DB993032
DB992868	DB992902	DB992945	DB992992#	DB993034*
DB992869	DB992903	DB992946	DB992996	DB993035
DB992870	DB992904*	DB992952	DB992998	DB993036*
DB992871	DB992905	DB992953*	DB992999#	DB993037*
DB992872	DB992908	DB992954	DB993000	DB993038
DB992874	DB992909	DB992957	DB993002#	DB993039*
DB992875	DB992911	DB992958	DB993003#	DB993040
DB992876*	DB992916	DB992959	DB993005	DB993041
DB992877	DB992917	DB992961	DB993008*	DB993042*
DB992878	DB992918	DB992962*	DB993009	DB993043
DB992879	DB992920	DB992965	DB993010	DB993044*
DB992880	DB992921	DB992966	DB993011	DB993045+
DB992881*	DB992922 (W)	DB992967#	DB993012	DB993046
DB992882*	DB992923	DB992969#	DB993014*	DB993047*
DB992883	DB992924	DB992970	DB993015	DB993048*
DB992884	DB992926	DB992972	DB993016*	DB993049
DB992886	DB992927	DB992974	DB993017	DB993052
DB992887	DB992929	DB992978	DB993018+	DB993054*
DB992888	DB992930*	DB992979	DB993019 (W)	DB993055*
DB992889	DB992932	DB992980#	DB993020	DB993056
DB992891	DB992934	DB992981#	DB993021	DB993057
DB992892	DB992935	DB992982#	DB993023	DB993058+
DB992893				

Number Series: DB993059 - DB993147

Description: 24T Ballast Hopper Wagon
Builder: Charles Roberts Ltd
Diagram No.: 1/587
Tare Weight: 11.5t 11.8t #
Design Code: ZF501B ZF501C #
Fishkind: "DOGFISH"

Lot No.: 2821
Built: 1956-57
G.L.W.: 36.5t
Tops Code: ZFV

DB993059	DB993078	DB993092	DB993110#	DB993124#
DB993060	DB993079	DB993096#	DB993111	DB993125#
DB993066	DB993080	DB993097#	DB993114#	DB993126
DB993068#	DB993081#	DB993098#	DB993116#	DB993127
DB993069#	DB993084	DB993101#	DB993117	DB993129#
DB993070	DB993087	DB993102	DB993119	DB993130#
DB993071	DB993088	DB993103#	DB993120#	DB993131#
DB993073#	DB993089#	DB993105#	DB993121#	DB993133
DB993074#	DB993090	DB993106#	DB993122#	DB993134

DB993136	DB993139	DB993144	DB993146#	DB993147#
DB993137	DB993140			

Number Series: DB993149 - DB993309

Description: 24T Ballast Hopper Wagon
Builder: Metropolitan Cammell Co Ltd — Lot No.: 2822
Diagram No.: 1/587 — Built: 1956-57
Tare Weight: 11.5t 11.8t # — G.L.W.: 36.5t
Design Code: ZF501A * ZF501B ZF501C # ZF501F + — Tops Code: ZFV ZFW +
Fishkind: "DOGFISH"

DB993149#	DB993188	DB993224	DB993258+	DB993286
DB993151	DB993192	DB993227#	DB993259	DB993287
DB993152	DB993193#	DB993228#(W)	DB993260	DB993288
DB993153	DB993194#	DB993229	DB993261	DB993289
DB993154	DB993197#	DB993230	DB993262*	DB993290*
DB993155#	DB993200#	DB993231#	DB993263	DB993292
DB993156#	DB993201#	DB993232	DB993265	DB993293*
DB993158#	DB993202#	DB993234	DB993268	DB993294
DB993161#	DB993203#	DB993236	DB993269	DB993295*
DB993162#	DB993204	DB993237	DB993270	DB993296
DB993165#(W)	DB993205#	DB993238#	DB993271	DB993297
DB993170#	DB993206	DB993241	DB993273*	DB993298
DB993173	DB993207#	DB993243#	DB993274	DB993299
DB993175#	DB993209	DB993244#	DB993275	DB993301*
DB993177#(W)	DB993210 (W)	DB993245#	DB993276*(W)	DB993302
DB993178#	DB993211	DB993248#	DB993277	DB993303
DB993179	DB993213	DB993249	DB993278*	DB993303*
DB993180#	DB993217#	DB993250	DB993280	DB993304
DB993181	DB993218#	DB993252	DB993281	DB993305
DB993183#	DB993219	DB993253	DB993282	DB993306
DB993184#	DB993221#	DB993255	DB993283	DB993307*
DB993186	DB993222	DB993256	DB993284	DB993308*
DB993187#	DB993223	DB993257	DB993285*	DB993309

Number Series: DB993311 - DB993470

Description: 24T Ballast Hopper Wagon
Builder: Metropolitan Cammell Co Ltd — Lot No.: 2823
Diagram No.: 1/587 — Built: 1957
Tare Weight: 11.5t — G.L.W.: 36.5t
Design Code: ZF501A * ZF501B ZF501F + — Tops Code: ZFV ZFW +
Fishkind: "DOGFISH"

DB993311	DB993322	DB993333	DB993345	DB993359
DB993312	DB993323	DB993334	DB993346	DB993360
DB993313	DB993324	DB993335*	DB993348*	DB993361
DB993314	DB993325*	DB993336	DB993349	DB993362
DB993315	DB993326	DB993338	DB993350	DB993363
DB993316	DB993327	DB993339	DB993351	DB993364
DB993317	DB993328	DB993340	DB993352	DB993365*
DB993318	DB993329	DB993341	DB993353	DB993367
DB993319*	DB993330	DB993342	DB993355	DB993368
DB993320	DB993331*	DB993343	DB993356	DB993369
DB993321	DB993332	DB993344	DB993358	DB993371

DB993372
DB993374
DB993375
DB993377
DB993379
DB993380
DB993381*
DB993383
DB993384
DB993385
DB993387
DB993388
DB993389
DB993390
DB993391
DB993392
DB993393
DB993394
DB993396
DB993397
DB993398
DB993399
DB993400
DB993401
DB993404+
DB993405
DB993406
DB993409
DB993410
DB993411
DB993412
DB993413
DB993415
DB993417
DB993419
DB993420
DB993421
DB993422*
DB993423
DB993424
DB993425
DB993427
DB993428
DB993429
DB993430
DB993431
DB993432
DB993433
DB993434
DB993435
DB993436
DB993437*
DB993438
DB993439
DB993440*
DB993441
DB993442
DB993443*
DB993444*
DB993445*
DB993446
DB993447
DB993448*
DB993449
DB993450
DB993451
DB993452
DB993453
DB993454
DB993455
DB993457
DB993459
DB993460
DB993461
DB993462
DB993463
DB993464
DB993465
DB993466
DB993467
DB993468
DB993469*
DB993470

<u>Number Series: DB993473 - DB993507</u>

Description: 24T Ballast Hopper Wagon
Builder: Metropolitan Cammell Co Ltd
Diagram No.: 1/587
Tare Weight: 11.5t
Design Code: ZF501A * ZF501B
Fishkind: "DOGFISH"

Lot No.: 2824
Built: 1957-58
G.L.W.: 36.5t
Tops Code: ZFV

DB993473
DB993474
DB993475*
DB993476
DB993477
DB993478
DB993479
DB993480
DB993481
DB993482
DB993484
DB993485
DB993486
DB993487
DB993488
DB993489
DB993490
DB993491
DB993492
DB993494
DB993495
DB993496*
DB993497
DB993498
DB993499
DB993502
DB993503
DB993505*
DB993506*
DB993507

<u>Number Series: DB993508 - DB993562</u>

Description: 19T Ballast Hopper Wagon
Builder: Metropolitan Cammell Co Ltd
Diagram No.: 1/586
Tare Weight: 9.8t 10.6t #
Design Code: ZE500A ZE500B + ZE500C * ZC008A #
Fishkind: "CATFISH" "PUFFIN" #

Lot No.: 2925
Built: 1956
G.L.W.: 30.0t
Tops Code: ZEV ZCV #

DB993508
DB993510+
DB993511*
DB993512+
DB992514+
DB993516+
DB993518+
DB993519
DB993520+
DB993521
DB993522+
DB993523+
DB993524
DB993526+
DB993527#
DB993528+
DB993529+
DB993530
DB993531+
DB993532+
DB993533+
DB993534+
DB993535
DB993536+
DB993537+
DB993539+
DB993540+
DB993541
DB993544+
DB993545+
DB993548
DB993549+
DB993550
DB993551+
DB993552+
DB993553
DB993557
DB993558+
DB993559+
DB993561+
DB993562

Number Series: DB993567 - DB993634

Description: 24T Ballast Hopper Wagon
Builder: BR (Shildon Works) Lot No.: 3255
Diagram No.: 1/587 Built: 1960
Tare Weight: 11.5t 11.8t # G.L.W.: 36.5t
Design Code: ZF501B ZF501C # Tops Code: ZFV
Fishkind: "DOGFISH"

DB993567+	DB993583+	DB993594+	DB993610	DB993625
DB993568+	DB993584+	DB993595	DB993611	DB993626
DB993569	DB993585+	DB993596	DB993613	DB993627
DB993571	DB993586+	DB993597	DB993615	DB993628
DB993574	DB993587+	DB993598	DB993616	DB993629
DB993575	DB993588	DB993599	DB993619	DB993630
DB993576+	DB993589+	DB993604	DB993621	DB993631
DB993577+	DB993590	DB993606	DB993622	DB993632
DB993579	DB993591+	DB993607	DB993623	DB993633
DB993580+	DB993593+	DB993608	DB993624	DB993634
DB993582+(W)				

Number Series: DB993706 - DB993707

Description: 16T Ballast Brake Van
Builder: R Y Pickering Ltd Lot No.: 2186
Diagram No.: 1/596 Built: 1950
Tare Weight: 16t G.L.W.: 16t
Design Code: ZU500B Tops Code: ZUP
Fishkind: "OYSTER"

DB993706 DB993707

Number Series: DB993710 - DB993711

Description: 20T Ballast Brake Van
Builder: BR (Derby Works) Lot No.: 2186
Diagram No.: 1/597 Built: 1952
Tare Weight: 20.5t G.L.W.: 20.5t
Design Code: ZU501A Tops Code: ZUV
Fishkind: "SHARK"

DB993710 DB993711

Number Series: DB993714 - DB993726

Description: 20T Ballast Brake Van
Builder: Birmingham R C & W Co Ltd Lot No.: 2431
Diagram No.: 1/597 Built: 1956
Tare Weight: 20.5t G.L.W.: 20.5t
Design Code: ZU501A ZU501G + ZU501Q * Tops Code: ZUV ZUW +*
Fishkind: "SHARK"

DB993714+	DB993717	DB993721	DB993723+	DB993725
DB993715+	DB993718	DB993722+	DB993724	DB993726
DB993716	DB993719*			

Number Series: DB993727 - DB993755

Description: 20T Ballast Brake Van
Builder: Birmingham R C & W Co Ltd
Lot No.: 2536
Diagram No.: 1/597
Built: 1956
Tare Weight: 20.5t
G.L.W.: 20.5t
Design Code: ZU501A ZU501G +
Tops Code: ZUV ZUW +
Fishkind: "SHARK"

DB993727	DB993733	DB993740+	DB993746+	DB993750 (W)
DB993728	DB993734+	DB993742+	DB993747+	DB993752+
DB993729	DB993736	DB993744	DB993748+	DB993753
DB993731	DB993737	DB993745+	DB993749+	DB993755
DB993732	DB993738			

Number Series: DB993758 - DB993783

Description: 20T Ballast Brake Van
Builder: Birmingham R C & W Co Ltd
Lot No.: 2536
Diagram No.: 1/597
Built: 1956
Tare Weight: 20.5t
G.L.W.: 20.5t
Design Code: ZU501A ZU501G +
Tops Code: ZUV ZUW +
Fishkind: "SHARK"

DB993758	DB993762+	DB993765 (W)	DB993770	DB993778
DB993760+	DB993763	DB993767	DB993774	DB993782
DB993761	DB993764+	DB993769	DB993777	DB993783

Number Series: DB993784 - DB993807

Description: 20T Ballast Brake Van
Builder: Birmingham R C & W Co Ltd
Lot No.: 2782
Diagram No.: 1/597
Built: 1956-57
Tare Weight: 20.5t
G.L.W.: 20.5t
Design Code: ZU501A ZU501G + ZU501H #
Tops Code: ZUV ZUW +#
Fishkind: "SHARK"

DB993784	DB993788	DB993792	DB993799	DB993804
DB993785	DB993790+	DB993795	DB993800#	DB993806
DB993786	DB993791	DB993796	DB993803	DB993807

Number Series: DB993816 - DB993856

Description: 20T Ballast Brake Van
Builder: Birmingham R C & W Co Ltd
Lot No.: 2931
Diagram No.: 1/597
Built: 1957
Tare Weight: 20.5t
G.L.W.: 20.5t
Design Code: ZU501A ZU501F % ZU501G + ZU501P !
Tops Code: ZUV ZUW +%!
Fishkind: "SHARK"

DB993816	DB993822	DB993829	DB993833+	DB993839
DB993817+	DB993823!	DB993830+	DB993834+	DB993840%
DB993819	DB993826	DB993831	DB993835	DB993841
DB993820	DB993827+	DB993832+	DB993836+	DB993842!

DB993843	DB993846	DB993850	DB993853	DB993855
DB993844 (W)	DB993847	DB993852	DB993854+	DB993856
DB993845				

Number Series: DB993857 - DB993904

Description: 20T Ballast Brake Van
Builder: Birmingham R C & W Co Ltd — Lot No.: 3040
Diagram No.: 1/597 — Built: 1957
Tare Weight: 20.5t — G.L.W.: 20.5t
Design Code: ZU501A — Tops Code: ZUV
Fishkind: "SHARK"

DB993857	DB993867	DB993879	DB993886	DB993895
DB993858	DB993868 (W)	DB993880	DB993887	DB993900
DB993859	DB993871	DB993881	DB993888	DB993901
DB993860	DB993873	DB993882	DB993891	DB993902
DB993861	DB993874	DB993883	DB993893	DB993904
DB993863	DB993876	DB993884		

Number Series: DB993905 - DB993920

Description: 20T Ballast Brake Van
Builder: Birmingham R C & W Co Ltd — Lot No.: 3150
Diagram No.: 1/597 — Built: 1958-59
Tare Weight: 20.5t — G.L.W.: 20.5t
Design Code: ZU501K ZU501L = ZU501M * — Tops Code: ZUV ZUW =*
Fishkind: "SHARK"

DB993905=	DB993908*	DB993914*	DB993916	DB993919*
DB993906	DB993913=	DB993915	DB993918=	DB993920
DB993907				

Number Series: DB993921 - DB993939

Description: 20T Ballast Brake Van
Builder: Central Wagon Co Ltd — Lot No.: 3285
Diagram No.: 1/598 — Built: 1962
Tare Weight: 20.5t — G.L.W.: 20.5t
Design Code: ZU501E ZU501J * ZU501N = — Tops Code: ZUV ZUW *
Fishkind: "SHARK"

DB993921	DB993925	DB993928=	DB993933	DB993937*
DB993922	DB993926	DB993929	DB993934	DB993938
DB993923	DB993927*	DB993931 (W)	DB993935	DB993939*
DB993924				

Number Series: DB994090 - DB994200

Description: 50T Bogie Ballast Wagon
Builder: Head Wrightson Ltd
Diagram No.: 1/645
Tare Weight: 28.3t 28.5t :
Design Code: YB500W ! YB501C % YB501P
YF008C + YF008F - YP001A *
YP001E = YX049A # YY045A :
Fishkind: "STURGEON" "TENCH" *=>

Lot No.: 2895
Built: 1956
G.L.W.: 40.0t # 79.3t
79.5t :
Tops Code: YBA YFA +-
YPA *=> YXA #
YYR :

DB994090#	DB994110	DB994132	DB994158	DB994181
DB994091*	DB994115%	DB994133	DB994159+(W)	DB994183+
DB994093	DB994117	DB994141	DB994163+	DB994184
DB994098*	DB994121+	DB994142	DB994166	DB994189!
DB994099-	DB994122+	DB994144	DB994168-	DB994190
DB994102	DB994123=	DB994146	DB994171%	LDB994192:
DB994103!	DB994124=	DB994148	DB994172	DB994194!
DB994104	DB994127 (W)	DB994149+	DB994173	DB994195!
DB994106	DB994128*	DB994151+	DB994175*	DB994196*
DB994108	DB994129	DB994155%	DB994180	DB994200!
DB994109%	DB994131	DB994157		

Number Series: DB994201 - DB994310

Description: 50T Bogie Ballast Wagon
Builder: Head Wrightson Ltd
Diagram No.: 1/647
Tare Weight: 28.3t z 29.4t
Design Code: YB500J = YB500Q * YB500S -
YB500U YB500V : YB500Z ^
YB501F z YF007D + YF007E %
YF007F > YF007G x YP001D !
YP001F # YP001H y YX048B $
Fishkind: "STURGEON" "TENCH" #!y

Lot No.: 2937
Built: 1956
G.L.W.: 79.3t z 80.4t
80.5t -^:>xy
Tops Code: YBA YFA %+>x
YXA $ YPA #!y

DB994201+	DB994224*	DB994245	DB994267!	DB994290
DB994202%	DB994225#	DB994247	DB994268*	DB994291*
DB994203#	DB994227>	DB994249*	DB994270+	DB994292=
DB994206*	DB994229=	DB994250%	DB994271%	DB994293!
DB994207#	DB994230:	DB994252*	DB994276z	DB994295*(W)
DB994208:	DB994231	DB994254x	DB994277^	DB994299
DB994209$	DB994232*	DB994255#	DB994278:	DB994300*
DB994212*	DB994235-	DB994257*	DB994279:	DB994303
DB994215*	DB994236 (W)	DB994259y	DB994281*	DB994305
DB994216*	DB994237*	DB994260!	DB994282!	DB994306
DB994217#	DB994239!	DB994261*(W)	DB994285*	DB994307*(W)
DB994218!	DB994240$	DB994262*	DB994286 (W)	DB994308
DB994220*	DB994242:	DB994266*(W)	DB994288*(W)	DB994310
DB994222:				

Number Series: DB994312 - DB994389

Description: 50T Bogie Ballast Wagon
Builder: Head Wrightson Ltd
Diagram No.: 1/647
Tare Weight: 29.4t 29.5t +
Design Code: YB500Q * YB500U YF007E %
YP001H = YP001F # YX048B $
YY045B +
Fishkind: "STURGEON" "TENCH" =#

Lot No.: 3047
Built: 1957
G.L.W.: 80.4t 80.5t y:
Tops Code: YBA YFA %
YPA =# YXA $
YYR +

DB994312*(W)	DB994328*	DB994344*(W)	DB994362	DB994378%
DB994313	DB994330*	DB994345*	DB994363*(W)	DB994379*
DB994317*(W)	DB994331	DB994346*(W)	DB994365 (W)	DB994382*
DB994318*	DB994332=	DB994350*	DB994366#	DB994383*
DB994319*(W)	DB994333	LDB994351+	DB994367	DB994384*
DB994320	DB994335*	DB994352*	DB994368*	DB994385*(W)
DB994325	DB994337	DB994355*(W)	DB994369*	DB994386
DB994326*	DB994339*(W)	DB994356*	DB994371*	DB994387 (W)
DB994327*	DB994341$	DB994357=	DB994377	DB994389#

Number Series: DB994392 - DB994421

Description: 50T Bogie Ballast Wagon
Builder: BR (Lancing Works)
Diagram No.: 1/647
Tare Weight: 29.4t
Design Code: YB500A * YB500D YF007E %
YP001C = YP001D ! YP001F #
Fishkind: "STURGEON" "TENCH" #!=

Lot No.: 3264
Built: 1960
G.L.W.: 80.4t
Tops Code: YBA YFA %
YPA =!#

DB994392*	DB994402*(W)	DB994407%	DB994413=	DB994419*
DB994396*	DB994405*	DB994410	DB994417*(W)	DB994420#
DB994398*	DB994406#	DB994411*(W)	DB994418!	DB994421*
DB994399*				

Number Series: DB994423 - DB994467

Description: 50T Bogie Ballast Wagon
Builder: BR (Lancing Works)
Diagram No.: 1/647
Tare Weight: 29.4t
Design Code: YB500A * YB500J < YB500R +
YB500U = YB501D YB501G -
YF007E % YP001D ! YP001F #
Fishkind: "STURGEON" "TENCH" #!

Lot No.: 3265
Built: 1960
G.L.W.: 80.4t
Tops Code: YBA YBB +
YFA % YPA !#

DB994423*	DB994430+	DB994441+	DB994450*(W)	DB994459+
DB994424*	DB994431*(W)	DB994443	DB994452<	DB994462-
DB994425*	DB994434*	DB994444	DB994453*	DB994464-
DB994428=	DB994435#	DB994446	DB994456*	DB994465+
DB994429!	DB994440%	DB994447-	DB994457+	DB994467

Number Series: DB994470

Description: 50T Bogie Ballast Wagon
Builder: BR (Lancing Works)
Diagram No.: 1/647
Tare Weight: 29.4t
Design Code: YB500Q
Fishkind: "STURGEON"

Lot No.: 3342
Built: 1960
G.L.W.: 80.4t
Tops Code: YBA

DB994470 (W)

Number Series: DB994500 - DB994530

Description: 50T Bogie Ballast Wagon
Builder: Head Wrightson Ltd
Diagram No: 1/638
Tare Weight: 26.0t % 27.0t
Design Code: YB500A % YB500G + YB500X
YP001J * YP001K #
Fishkind: "STURGEON" "TENCH" *#

Lot No.: 2322
Built: 1952-53
G.L.W.: 77.0t % 78.0t
Tops Code: YBA YBO %
YPA *#

DB994500+(W)	DB994504+	DB994506#	DB994508	DB994530%(W)
DB994503+	DB994505*	DB994507	DB994524	

Number Series: DB994595 - DB994653

Description: 50T Bogie Ballast Wagon
Builder: Head Wrightson Ltd
Diagram No.: 1/638
Tare Weight: 26.0t 27.0t = 28.3t +
Design Code: YB500N YB500X = YB501A #
YB501C +
Fishkind: "STURGEON"

Lot No.: 2404
Built: 1953-54
G.L.W.: 77.0t 78.0t =
79.3t #+
Tops Code: YBA

DB994595	DB994628	DB994647+	DB994650=	DB994653#
DB994606 (W)				

Number Series: DB994717 - DB994854

Description: 50T Bogie Ballast Wagon
Builder: Head Wrightson Ltd
Diagram No.: 1/645
Tare Weight: 28.3t
Design Code: YB500B - YB500H # YB500P
YB500W % YB500Y + YB501C :
YP001A * YX049C !
Fishkind: "STURGEON" "TENCH" *

Lot No.: 2407
Built: 1955
G.L.W.: 40.0t ! 79.3t
Tops Code: YBA YBO -
YPA * YXA !

DB994717!	DB994744	DB994783	DB994818 (W)	DB994830
DB994724	DB994752*	DB994784+	DB994820	DB994835
DB994728 (W)	DB994757	DB994788 (W)	DB994821	DB994840
DB994731	DB994758*	DB994793%	DB994823	DB994845
DB994732	DB994770#	DB994794:	DB994828	DB994849
DB994738+	DB994777 (W)	DB994795	DB994829 (W)	DB994854
DB994739*	DB994781-	DB994803:		

Number Series: DB994861 - DB994982

Description: 50T Bogie Ballast Wagon
Builder: Head Wrightson Ltd
Diagram No.: 1/645
Tare Weight: 28.3t
Design Code: YB500H # YB500P YB500W %
YB500Y ! YB501C * YB501F +
YP001B = YX049D >
Fishkind: "STURGEON" "TENCH" =

Lot No.: 2614
Built: 1955
G.L.W.: 79.3t
Tops Code: YBA YPA =
YXA >

DB994861=	DB994890!	DB994919	DB994941%(W)	DB994973
DB994866	DB994892*	DB994920	DB994942	DB994976*(W)
DB994868#(W)	DB994898=	DB994929!	DB994943	DB994977*
DB994884#	DB994900	DB994938+	DB994957*	DB994978>
DB994885=	DB994903	DB994939	DB994962	DB994981
DB994886	DB994904=	DB994940	DB994970 (W)	DB994982

Number Series: DB995505 - DB995512

Description: 14T Sleeper Wagon
Builder: BR (Swindon Works)
Diagram No.: 1/620
Tare Weight: 19.0t
Design Code: ZX510A
Fishkind: "MINNOW"

Lot No.: 2081
Built: 1949
G.L.W.: 46.0t
Tops Code: ZXV

DB995505 DB995507 DB995508 DB995512

Number Series: DB995515 - DB995520

Description: 14T Sleeper Wagon
Builder: BR (Swindon Works)
Diagram No: 1/620
Tare Weight: 19.0t
Design Code: ZX510A
Fishkind: "MINNOW"

Lot No.: 2093
Built: 1949
G.L.W.: 46.0t
Tops Code: ZXV

DB995515 DB995516 DB995520

Number Series: DB996028 - DB996070

Description: 50T Bogie Rail Wagon
Builder: Teeside S & E Co Ltd
Diagram No: 1/640
Tare Weight: 24.2t
Design Code: YM500X
Fishkind: "SALMON"

Lot No.: 2216
Built: 1951-52
G.L.W.: 75.0T
Tops Code: YMA

DB996028 DB996054 DB996066 DB996070

Number Series: DB996100 - DB996151

Description: 50T Bogie Rail Wagon
Builder: Head Wrightson Ltd
Diagram No.: 1/642
Tare Weight: 27.4t 28.25t + 28.55t #
28.6t %
Design Code: YF001B # YF001C % YM501B +
YM501D YB501J *

Lot No.: 2363
Built: 1952
G.L.W.: 78.4t 79.0t +
Tops Code: YMA YMB +
YFA #%
Fishkind: "SALMON"

DB996100	DB996110	DB996120	DB996131	DB996142
DB996101	DB996112	DB996121	DB996132%	DB996143
DB996102	DB996113#	DB996122	DB996134	DB996144
DB996103	DB996114#	DB996123	DB996135	DB996145
DB996104	DB996115	DB996124	DB996136	DB996146
DB996105	DB996116	DB996125	DB996137*	DB996147 (W)
DB996106+	DB996117	DB996127	DB996139	DB996148
DB996107*	DB996118	DB996128	DB996140	DB996150#
DB996109%	DB996119+	DB996130%	DB996141*	DB996151*

Number Series: DB996169 - DB996205

Description: 50T Bogie Rail Wagon
Builder: Teeside S & E Co Ltd
Diagram No.: 1/640
Tare Weight: 24.2t
Design Code: YM500X
Fishkind: "SALMON"

Lot No.: 2399
Built: 1952-53
G.L.W.: 75.0t
Tops Code: YMA

DB996169 (W)	DB996181	DB996185	DB996205

Number Series: DB996214 - DB996308

Description: 50T Bogie Rail Wagon
Builder: Head Wrightson Ltd
Diagram No.: 1/642
Tare Weight: 27.4t 28.4t :%#
Design Code: YF001A : YF001B # YF001C %
YF010A > YM501D YM501J *
YM502E !

Lot No.: 2534
Built: 1954-55
G.L.W.: 78.4t
Tops Code: YMA YFA >#%
YFO :
Fishkind: "SALMON"

DB996214	DB996232	DB996250:	DB996273#	DB996292*
DB996215	DB996233%	DB996252	DB996274	DB996293
DB996216	DB996234	DB996253	DB996277#	DB996294*
DB996217	DB996236	DB996256	DB996278	DB996298
DB996219	DB996237*	DB996258%	DB996279	DB996300!
DB996220	DB996238	DB996260%	DB996281	DB996301*(W)
DB996223	DB996240*	DB996264%	DB996282	DB996302#
DB996225	DB996241	DB996265#	DB996283*	DB996303
DB996226	DB996242	DB996267*	DB996284*	DB996304*
DB996227	DB996243#	DB996268	DB996286	DB996305*
DB996228#	DB996246:	DB996270	DB996287>	DB996306*
DB996229*	DB996247	DB996271	DB996289	DB996307*
DB996230	DB996248	DB996272*	DB996291	DB996308
DB996231:	DB996249			

Number Series: DB996309 - DB996362

Description: 50T Bogie Rail Wagon
Builder: G R Turner Ltd — Lot No.: 2615
Diagram No: 1/644 — Built: 1954-55
Tare Weight: 26.4t 27.4t +# — G.L.W.: 78.4t
Design Code: YF002B + YF002C # YM501G YM501N - YM501R * — Tops Code: YMA YFA +#
Fishkind: "SALMON"

DB996309	DB996321	DB996330	DB996342	DB996355
DB996310	DB996322+	DB996331	DB996345+	DB996356-
DB996311	DB996323-	DB996332-	DB996347+	DB996357
DB996312	DB996324	DB996333	DB996348	DB996358
DB996313	DB996325#	DB996334+	DB996349	DB996359+
DB996314	DB996326	DB996335#	DB996350	DB996360
DB996315	DB996327	DB996338-	DB996351	DB996361
DB996319 *	DB996328	DB996341	DB996353	DB996362
DB996320 +				

Number Series: DB996363 - DB996420

Description: 50T Bogie Rail Wagon
Builder: G R Turner Ltd — Lot No.: 2894
Diagram No: 1/646 — Built: 1956
Tare Weight: 27.4t 28.4t * — G.L.W.: 78.4t
Design Code: YF003B * YM500N YM500Y % YM501H ! YM501K = YM502A # YM502C - YM502D : — Tops Code: YMA YMB <:% YFA #^!
Fishkind: "SALMON"

DB996363	DB996374	DB996387	DB996401*	DB996411-
DB996364	DB996375	DB996388*	DB996402:	DB996412=
DB996365	DB996376!	DB996389=	DB996403%	DB996413
DB996366!	DB996378!	DB996390=	DB996404#	DB996414%
DB996367=	DB996379	DB996391%	DB996405=	DB996415-
DB996368%	DB996380=	DB996394	DB996406=	DB996416 (W)
DB996369%	DB996381=	DB996395=	DB996407=	DB996417%
DB996370%	DB996382	DB996397*	DB996408	DB996418=
DB996371%	DB996384=	DB996398=	DB996409	DB996419%
DB996372%	DB996385	DB996399#	DB996410=	DB996420=
DB996373=	DB996386!	DB996400		

Number Series: DB996421 - DB996518

Description: 50T Bogie Rail Wagon
Builder: G R Turner Ltd — Lot No.: 2926
Diagram No.: 1/646 — Built: 1952
Tare Weight: 27.4t 27.5t <: 28.4t ! 29.4t $ — G.L.W.: 78.4t 78.5t <:
Design Code: YF003B ! YF006A # YF006B ^ YM500N YM500Y * YM501C < YM501H - YM501K = YM501M : YM501P % YM502D > YX062A $ — Tops Code: YMA YMB <:% YFA #^
Fishkind: "SALMON"

DB996421	DB996424	DB996427	DB996430*	DB996433=
DB996422	DB996425=	DB996428	DB996431	DB996434
DB996423=(W)	DB996426	DB996429=(W)	DB996432#	DB996435:

DB996436	DB996455=	DB996472=	DB996489	DB996504*
DB996439	DB996457<	DB996473	DB996490^	DB996505*(W)
DB996440=	DB996458	DB996474	DB996491	DB996506*
DB996441%	DB996459-	DB996475=	DB996492	DB996507=
DB996442!	DB996460=	DB996476$	DB996493!	DB996508
DB996443!	DB996461	DB996477	DB996494*	DB996509*
DB996445%	DB996462	DB996478!	DB996495!	DB996510
DB996446!	DB996463=	DB996480!	DB996496-	DB996511-
DB996447	DB996464	DB996481!	DB996497=	DB996512*
DB996448*	DB996465#	DB996482=	DB996498*	DB996513!
DB996449>	DB996466>	DB996483	DB996499	DB996514
DB996450	DB996467	DB996484*	DB996500=	DB996515*
DB996451=	DB996468^	DB996485=	DB996501=	DB996516=
DB996452=	DB996469=	DB996486=	DB996502!	DB996517<
DB996453	DB996470	DB996487=	DB996503*	DB996518=
DB996454=	DB996471=	DB996488^		

Number Series: DB996519 - DB996597

Description: 50T Bogie Rail Wagon
Builder: Teeside S & E Co Ltd — Lot No.: 3065
Diagram No.: 1/646 — Built: 1958
Tare Weight: 27.4t 27.5t < 28.4t ! — G.L.W.: 78.4t 78.5t <
Design Code: YF003B ! YF006B ^ YM500N # YM500Y * YM501C < YM501H - YM501K YM501P % YM502A >
Tops Code: YMA YMB <% YFA ^!
Fishkind: "SALMON"

DB996519	DB996538	DB996553!	DB996568-	DB996583
DB996520^	DB996539#	DB996554*	DB996569	DB996584#
DB996521-	DB996540%	DB996555	DB996570	DB996585
DB996523	DB996541*	DB996556#	DB996571	DB996586*
DB996524	DB996542*	DB996557	DB996572	DB996587#
DB996525*	DB996543	DB996558>	DB996573	DB996588
DB996526*	DB996544#	DB996559-	DB996574#	DB996589
DB996527!	DB996545	DB996560	DB996575	DB996590
DB996528	DB996546%	DB996561*	DB996576<	DB996591#
DB996529!	DB996547#	DB996562#	DB996577#	DB996592
DB996530	DB996548#	DB996563*	DB996578#	DB996593
DB996531-	DB996549	DB996564!	DB996579#	DB996594#
DB996533	DB996550#	DB996565	DB996580#	DB996595^
DB996534*	DB996551!	DB996566!	DB996581^	DB996596#
DB996535*	DB996552	DB996567#	DB996582-	DB996597

Number Series: DB996598 - DB996677

Description: 50T Bogie Rail Wagon
Builder: G R Turner Ltd — Lot No.: 3067
Diagram No.: 1/646 — Built: 1957-58
Tare Weight: 27.4t 27.5t <- 28.4t ! — G.L.W.: 78.4t 78.5t <
Design Code: YF003B ! YF006B ^ YM500N # YM500Y * YM500D > YM501C < YM501H - YM501K YM502C +
Tops Code: YMA YMB < YMO > YFA #^!
Fishkind: "SALMON"

DB996598	DB996601*	DB996604#	DB996608*	DB996611*
DB996599!	DB996602#	DB996606!	DB996609#	DB996612#
DB996600	DB996603#	DB996607	DB996610	DB996613

DB996614
DB996615#
DB996616#
DB996617-
DB996618
DB996619#
DB996620
DB996621
DB996622#
DB996623
DB996624-(W)
DB996627-
DB996628#
DB996629#
DB996630^
DB996631#
DB996632
DB996633*
DB996634
DB996635<
DB996636*
DB996637^
DB996638#
DB996639
DB996640
DB996641*
DB996642
DB996643^
DB996644#
DB996645!
DB996646*
DB996647^
DB996648#
DB996649*
DB996650#
DB996651#
DB996652#
DB996653>
DB996654*
DB996655#
DB996656!
DB996657#
DB996659#
DB996660
DB996661
DB996662*
DB996663*
DB996664
DB996665
DB996666#
DB996667
DB996668*
DB996669
DB996670
DB996671*
DB996672-
DB996673+
DB996674*
DB996677*

Number Series: DB996699

Description: 50T Bogie Rail Wagon
Builder: BR (Shildon Works)
Tare Weight: 27.0t
Design Code: YM001A
Fishkind: "SALMON"
Lot No.: 4034
Built: 1983
G.L.W.: 80.0t
Tops Code:

DB996699

Number Series: DB996804 - DB996880

Description: 50T Bogie Rail Wagon
Builder: BR (Wolverton Works)
Diagram No.: 1/637
Tare Weight: 23.0t 29.0t = 29.1t #*
Design Code: YF004B # YF004C * YM501B = YM501E
Fishkind: "SALMON"
Lot No.: 3261
Built: 1959-60
G.L.W.: 74.0t 79.0t = 79.1t #*
Tops Code: YMA YMB = YFA # YFB *

DB996804=
DB996805
DB996806#
DB996807
DB996808#
DB996809#
DB996810#
DB996811=
DB996812*
DB996813#
DB996814
DB996815
DB996816#
DB996817
DB996818=
DB996819#
DB996820
DB996821
DB996822#
DB996823#
DB996824
DB996825=
DB996826
DB996827#
DB996828#
DB996830
DB996831#
DB996832#
DB996833
DB996834
DB996836#
DB996837
DB996838
DB996839
DB996840#
DB996841
DB996842
DB996843#
DB996844
DB996847#
DB996848
DB996849
DB996850
DB996851
DB996852
DB996853#
DB996855
DB996856#
DB996857
DB996858
DB996859
DB996860#
DB996861
DB996862
DB996864
DB996865
DB996866
DB996867
DB996868
DB996869
DB996872
DB996873
DB996875
DB996877
DB996878
DB996879
DB996880

Number Series: DB996882 - DB996921

Description: 50T Bogie Rail Wagon
Builder: BR (Wolverton Works)
Diagram No.: 1/637
Tare Weight: 23.0t 23.8t : 27.0t + 28.0t = 29.1t !
Design Code: YF004B ! YF005B : YF005C - YM500R + YM501A YM501B = YM501F * YM501Q #
Fishkind: "SALMON"

Lot No.: 3262
Built: 1960
G.L.W.: 73.8t : 74.0t 78.0t + 79.0t = 79.1t !
Tops Code: YMA #* YMB YFA -! YFB :

DB996882*	DB996893*	DB996900:	DB996908*	DB996915=
DB996884*	DB996894#	DB996901*	DB996909*	DB996916=
DB996885	DB996895-	DB996902*	DB996910*	DB996917=
DB996886	DB996896+	DB996903*	DB996911	DB996918=
DB996888*	DB996897#	DB996904	DB996912=	DB996919=
DB996890*	DB996898	DB996905*	DB996913=	DB996920=
DB996891-	DB996899*	DB996907*	DB996914!	DB996921=
DB996892*				

Number Series: DB996922 - DB996969

Description: 50T Bogie Rail Wagon
Builder: BR (Wolverton Works)
Diagram No.: 1/637
Tare Weight: 23.0t 23.8t ! 24.8t % 28.0t * 28.3t +
Design Code: YF005B ! YF005C : YM500Q > YM501A - YM501B * YM501E + YM501F = YM501L YM501Q ^ YX060A %

Lot No.: 3284
Built: 1961
G.L.W.: 73.8t ! 74.0t 79.0t = 79.3t +
Tops Code: YMA + YMB YFA : YFB ! YXA %
Fishkind: "SALMON"

DB996922+	DB996932+	DB996942	DB996951:	DB996961^
DB996923+	DB996933+	DB996943=	DB996953=	DB996962!
DB996924+	DB996934+	DB996944	DB996954=	DB996963=
DB996925+	DB996935+	DB996945%	DB996955=	DB996964>
DB996926+	DB996936+	DB996946-	DB996956=	DB996965:
DB996927*	DB996937=	DB996947=	DB996957=	DB996966-
DB996928+	DB996938=	DB996948:	DB996958=	DB996967+
DB996929+	DB996939	DB996949	DB996959=	DB996968+
DB996930*	DB996940-	DB996950-	DB996960!	DB996969:
DB996931+	DB996941			

Number Series: DB996970 - DB996994

Description: 50T Bogie Rail Wagon
Builder: Powell Duffryn Ltd
Diagram No.: 1/628
Tare Weight: 23.0t 24.8t % 27.0t +
Design Code: YM500Q + YM501A YM501F # YM501L % YM501Q * YX060A ^
Fishkind: "SALMON"

Lot No.: 3352
Built: 1962
G.L.W.: 74.0t 78.0t +
Tops Code: YMA +# YMB YXA >

DB996970#	DB996972#	DB996974%	DB996977	DB996979%
DB996971*	DB996973	DB996976#	DB996978#	DB996980#

DB996981#	DB996986	DB996989#	DB996991#	DB996993+
DB996983#	DB996987#	DB996990	DB996992#	DB996994#
DB996985>	DB996988#			

Number Series: DB996995 - DB997019

Description: 50T Bogie Rail Wagon
Builder: Head Wrightson Co Ltd
Diagram No.: 1/637
Tare Weight: 28.3t 29.0t * 29.1t +#=
Design Code: YF004B + YF004C = YF004D #
YM501B * YM501E
Fishkind: "SALMON"

Lot No.: 3353
Built: 1960-61
G.L.W.: 79.0t * 79.3t
79.1t +#=
Tops Code: YMA YMB *
YFA + YFB #=

DB996995#	DB997000	DB997006	DB997012*	DB997016
DB996996	DB997001	DB997008+	DB997013+	DB997017
DB996997=	DB997002	DB997009	DB997014+	DB997018+
DB996998	DB997003	DB997010	DB997015+	DB997019
DB996999	DB997005	DB997011		

Number Series: DB997801 - DB997822

Description: Bogie Spoil Skip Wagon
Builder: BR (Ashford Works)
Tare Weight: 26.0t
Design Code: YD001A
Fishkind: "SKATE"

Lot No.: 4005
Built: 1981
G.L.W.: 77.0t
Tops Code: YDA

DB997801	DB997806	DB997811	DB997815	DB997819
DB997802	DB997807	DB997812	DB997816	DB997820
DB997803	DB997808	DB997813	DB997817	DB997821
DB997804	DB997809	DB997814	DB997818	DB997822
DB997805	DB997810			

Number Series: DB998001 - DB998002

Description: 20T Flatrol Wagon
Builder: BR (Swindon Works)
Diagram No.: 2/900
Tare Weight: 13.5t
Design Code: ZX164A * ZX164B
Fishkind: "LORIOT"

Lot No.: 2095
Built: 1959
G.L.W.: 34.0t
Tops Code: ZXP

DB998001 DB998002*

Number Series: DB998003 - DB998005

Description: 20T Flatrol Wagon
Builder: BR (Swindon Works)
Diagram No.: 2/900
Tare Weight: 13.5t
Design Code: ZX164A
Fishkind: "LORIOT"

Lot No.: 2270
Built: 1952-53
G.L.W.: 34.0t
Tops Code: ZXP

DB998003 (W) DB998005

Number Series: DB998006

Description: 20T Flatrol Wagon
Builder: BR (Lancing Works)
Diagram No.: 2/903
Tare Weight: 15.7t
Design Code: ZV508C
Fishkind: "FLATROL"

Lot No.: 2951
Built: 1958
G.L.W.: 36.2t
Tops Code: ZVR

DB998006

Number Series: DB998007 - DB998009

Description: 20T Flatrol Wagon
Builder: BR (Swindon Works)
Diagram No.: 2/902
Tare Weight: 14.0t
Design Code: ZV506C
Fishkind: "LORIOT"

Lot No.: 2980
Built: 1958
G.L.W.: 34.5t
Tops Code: ZVP

DB998007 DB998009

Number Series: DB998014

Description: 20T Flatrol Wagon
Builder: BR (Swindon Works)
Diagram No.: 2/901
Tare Weight: 13.5t
Design Code: ZV506D
Fishkind: "LORIOT"

Lot No.: 3201
Built: 1959
G.L.W.: 34.0t
Tops Code: ZVP

DB998014

Number Series: DB998015 - DB998028

Description: 20T Flatrol Wagon
Builder: BR (Lancing Works)
Diagram No.: 2/904
Tare Weight: 11.5t
Design Code: ZV509A # ZV509B * ZX520C
Fishkind: "LORIOT"

Lot No.: 3257
Built: 1960
G.L.W.: 32.0t
Tops Code: ZVP # ZVR * ZXR

DB998015	DB998018*	DB998022*	DB998025	DB998028#
DB998017	DB998020	DB998024	DB998026	

Number Series: ADB998050

Description: 13T Flatrol Wagon (DEMU Engine Carrier)
Builder: BR (Ashford Works) Lot No.: 3077
Diagram No.: 1/635 Built: 1957
Tare Weight: 13.0t G.L.W.: 23.0t
Design Code: ZR515D Tops Code: ZRB

ADB998050

Number Series: ADB998051 - ADB998053

Description: 13T Flatrol Wagon (DEMU Engine Carrier)
Builder: BR (Ashford Works) Lot No.: 3114
Diagram No.: 1/635 Built: 1957
Tare Weight: 13.0t G.L.W.: 23.0t
Design Code: ZR515B * ZR515C Tops Code: ZRW * ZRX

ADB998051 ADB998052* ADB998053*

Number Series: DB998070 - DB998073

Description: 100T Girder Wagon Set
Builder: BR (Ashford Works) Lot No.: 3709
Diagram No.: 1/625 Built: 1970
Tare Weight: 12.0t G.L.W.: 63.0t
Design Code: YV501B Tops Code: YVO
Fishkind: "CONGER"

DB998070 DB998071 DB998072 DB998073

Number Series: DB998501 - DB998504

Description: Crane Match Wagon
Builder: BR (Ashford Works) Built: 1959
Diagram No.: 2/151 G.L.W.: 9.0t
Tare Weight: 9.0t Tops Code: ZSR
Design Code: ZS515D

DB998501 (W) DB998502 (W) DB998503 (W) DB998504

Number Series: DB998505 - DB998516

Description: Crane Match Wagon
Builder: BR (Lancing/Ashford Works) Built: 1962
Diagram No.: 1/624 +* 1/625 G.L.W.: 6.3t + 8.0t 10.0t #*
Tare Weight: 6.3t + 8.0t 10.0t #*
Design Code: ZS511B ZS511C # ZS515F + ZS515H * Tops Code: ZSR

DB998505 (W) DB998507 (W) DB998511+(W) DB998513*(W) DB998515*(W)
DB998506 (W) DB998508 DB998512 (W) DB998514#(W) DB998516#(W)

Number Series: DB998517 - DB998542

Description: Crane Match Wagon
Builder: Various
Tare Weight: 24.0t = 30.0t 32.6t *
Design Code: ZS311A # ZS314A = ZS314B
ZS511B *

Built: 1962-64
G.L.W.: 24.0t = 30.0t
32.6t *
Tops Code: ZSB ZSP =
ZSV #

ADB998517	ADB998531#	ADB998534	ADB998538	ADB998541 (W)
ADB998518	ADB998532*	ADB998535	ADB998539	ADB998542=
ADB998530#	ADB998533*	ADB998537=	ADB998540	

Number Series: DB998543 - DB998545

Description: Single Line Track Relaying Gantry Carrier
Builder: Motrak Co Ltd
Tare Weight: 70.0t
Design Code: YX509C
Tops Code: YXR

Lot No.: 3884
Built: 1979
G.L.W.: 70.0t

DB998543 DB998544 DB998545

Number Series: ADB998918 - ADB998919

Description: 14T 2 Axle Tank Wagon
Builder: Charles Roberts Co Ltd
Diagram No.: 1/633
Tare Weight: 14.0t
Design Code: ZR503C

Lot No.: 2372
Built: 1953
G.L.W.: 24.0t
Tops Code: ZRP

ADB998918 ADB998919

Number Series: LDB998933 - LDB998938

Description: 20T 2 Axle Tank Wagon
Builder: R Y Pickering Co Ltd
Diagram No.: 1/629
Tare Weight: 11.5t
Design Code: ZY094A ZY094B *

Lot No.: 3354
Built: 1960
G.L.W.: 32.0t
Tops Code: ZYP ZYR *

LDB998933 LDB998936* LDB998938

Number Series: ADB999021 - ADB999030

Description: 22T 2 Axle Tank Wagon
Builder: Charles Roberts Ltd
Cambrian Wagon Co Ltd #=
Tare Weight: 11.5t * 12.0t 12.5t =#
Design Code: ZR131C ZR132C = ZR134D #
ZR135B *

Lot No.: 3878
Built: 1958-59
G.L.W.: 35.0t 36.0t *
Tops Code: ZRW

ADB999021 ADB999027# ADB999028* ADB999029* ADB999030=(W)

Number Series: ADB999031

Description: 22T 2 Axle Tank Wagon
Builder: BR (Swindon Works)
Tare Weight: 14.0t
Design Code: ZR306B

Built: 1954
G.L.W.: 28.0t
Tops Code: ZRO

ADB999031

Number Series: DB999035 - DB999037

Description: 22T Axle Tank Wagon
Builder: W H Davis Ltd
Tare Weight: 13.0t
Design Code: ZR198A

Built: 1960
G.L.W.: 35.5t
Tops Code: ZRV

DB999035	(TEX47769)	DB999037	(TEX47761)

Number Series: ADB999066 - ADB999079

Description: 22T 2 Axle Tank Wagon
Builder: Cambrian Wagon Co Ltd
Tare Weight: 12.0t < 12.5t 13.0t >
Design Code: ZR131D < ZR132C * ZR134D
ZR134E > ZR195B =

Lot No.: 3977
Built: 1958-59
G.L.W.: 35.0t 35.5t >=
Tops Code: ZRG > ZRW

ADB999066*	(ESSO43953)	ADB999073=	( )	ADB999078>	(ESSO43617)
ADB999068*	(ESSO43724)	ADB999074	(ESSO43777)	ADB999079<	(ESSO43793)

Number Series: DB999097 - DB999099

Description: 22T 2 Axle Tank Wagon
Builder: Standard Wagon Co Ltd *
Norbrit-Pickering Ltd
Metropolitan Cammell Ltd +
Tare Weight: 11.5t 13.4t * 15.8t +
Design Code: ZR223A ZR224A + ZR225A *

Built: 1964-66
G.L.W.: 36.0t 46.0t *+
Tops Code: ZRA +* ZRF

DB999097	(IU083579)	DB999098+	(BRT57086)	DB999099*	( )

Number Series: DB999101 - DB999104

Description: 22T 2 Axle Tank Wagon
Builder: Norbrit-Pickering Ltd
Tare Weight: 13.2t
Design Code: ZR226A

Built: 1966-67
G.L.W.: 46.0t
Tops Code: ZRA

DB999101	DB999102	DB999103	DB999104

Number Series: DB999105

Description: 22T 2 Axle Tank Wagon
Builder: Norbrit-Pickering Ltd
Tare Weight: 11.5t
Design Code: ZR136A

Built: 1965
G.L.W.: 36.0t
Tops Code: ZRV

DB999105 (ESSO45258)

Number Series: DB999106 - DB999112

Description: 2 Axle Tank Wagon
Builder: Metropolitan Cammell Ltd
Tare Weight: 16.3t +* 16.5t
Design Code: ZR239A ZR240A * ZR241A +

Built: 1965-66
G.L.W.: 46.0t
Tops Code: ZRA

DB999106 (SUKO61114)
DB999107 (SUKO61116)
DB999108 (SUKO61139)
DB999109 (SUKO61140)
DB999110 (SUKO61206)
DB999111* (SUKO61503)
DB999112+ (SUKO61527)

Number Series: DB999900

Description: COV-AB "Tribometer" Test Vehicle
Builder: BR (Shildon Works)
Tare Weight: 19.0t
Design Code: ZX100C
Tops Code: ZXR

Lot No.: 3722
Built: 1971
G.L.W.: 19.0t

RDB999900

Also Available from South Coast Transport Publishing

British Rail Wagon Fleet
British Railways ("B" - Prefixed Freight Stock)
@£6.95

Departmental Coaching Stock
@£6.95

British Rail Internal Users
@£7.95

R.I.V. Wagon Fleet
@£5.95

These publications and further copies of Engineers Series Wagon Fleet @ £6.95 per copy (all prices inc. post & packing) may be obtained from our Mail Order Dept. at the address below:-

33, Porchester Road,
Woolston,
Southampton,
Hampshire SO19 7JB

Please make cheques and postal orders payable to S.C.T. Publishing.

Trade enquiries are welcomed and these should be sent to:-

3, Morley Drive,
Bishop's Waltham,
Hampshire SO32 1RX

* * * * * * * * * *

COVER PHOTOGRAPHS

Front:-

ZRA DB999103 is an example of the 2 Axle Tank Wagons that have been acquired second hand by BR for Departmental Service from the Private Owner Fleets. It is pictured at Wellingborough on 19th February 1989.
Paul W. Bartlett

Rear (Upper):-

DB996965, tops code YFA and fishkind "Salmon", a 50T Bogie Rail Wagon is seen at Tees Yard on 25th September 1988. Paul W. Bartlett

Rear (Lower):-

Pictured at York on 20th August 1985 is Bogie Spoil Skip Wagon, "Skate", YDA, DB997820. Paul W. Bartlett